BRACHIOPODA OF THE KEYSER LIMESTONE (SILURIAN–DEVONIAN) OF MARYLAND AND ADJACENT AREAS

*The printing of this volume
has been made possible by the
Henry R. Aldrich Publication Fund
of The Geological Society of America*

The Geological Society of America, Inc.
Memoir 102

BRACHIOPODA
OF THE
KEYSER LIMESTONE
(SILURIAN-DEVONIAN)
OF MARYLAND AND
ADJACENT AREAS

By

ZEDDIE PAUL BOWEN

University of Rochester, Rochester, New York

Made in the United States of America

PUBLISHED BY
THE GEOLOGICAL SOCIETY OF AMERICA, INC.
231 East 46th Street
New York, New York 10017

Design and Production by Technipress, Inc.
Manufactured by Port City Press, Inc.

ACKNOWLEDGMENTS

It is a pleasure to acknowledge my indebtedness to Dr. H. B. Whittington of Harvard University for his extensive advice and guidance during this project, and for his inspiring teaching which first interested me in paleontology. This study was done under Dr. Whittington in partial fulfillment of the requirements for the degree of Doctor of Philosophy at Harvard University. It was submitted in April 1963.

I owe a special debt to Dr. A. J. Boucot of the California Institute of Technology for originally suggesting the problem, for his extensive and enthusiastic help and encouragement, for making available copies of several papers in press, and for making me aware of some of the intricacies of brachiopod paleontology.

Thanks are also given to Dr. J. M. Berdan of the U.S. Geological Survey for critically reading the manuscript, for sending me copies of the plates of several papers in preparation, and for her many helpful comments. I thank Dr. T. W. Amsden of the Oklahoma Geological Survey for reading the manuscript and making many suggestions to improve it; Dr. G. A. Cooper for suggestions concerning brachiopod taxonomy and for making available type specimens in the U.S. National Museum; Dr. D. M. Raup of the Johns Hopkins University for his early contribution to my understanding of fossils and for loaning that university's collection of brachiopods; and Dr. Bernhard Kummel of Harvard University for discussion and advice on various parts of the project.

Special thanks are due my wife, Dorothy, who was my field assistant in 1960 and 1961, and who aided in the preparation of the specimens, in typing, editing, and proofreading the manuscript, and made many helpful suggestions.

Funds for summer field work during 1960–61 were granted from the Louise H. Daly Fund, Harvard University, for which I am grateful.

CONTENTS

ILLUSTRATIONS

PLATES

FIGURES

TABLE

ABSTRACT

The brachiopod fauna of the Keyser Limestone within a 50-mile radius of the type section at Keyser, West Virginia, is described. Thirty-three species representing 26 genera are recognized in the fauna; six species are new: *Rhynchospirina martinensis* and *R. newcreekensis, Delthyris hyndmanensis, Nanothyris boucoti, Rhynchotreta? hancockensis,* and *Machaeraria whittingtoni.*

A new name, the New Creek Limestone, is proposed for the rock-stratigraphic unit referred to as the Coeymans Limestone in Maryland and West Virginia. The type section is at New Creek, West Virginia.

The two faunal zones of the Keyser, the *Eccentricosta jerseyensis* Zone in the lower part and the *Meristella praenuntia* Zone in the upper part, are redescribed, and use of the "subzone" terminology previously employed for the formation is discouraged. The name, *Meristella praenuntia* Zone, is proposed to replace the inappropriate, older name, *Favosites helderbergiae praecedens* Zone, for the upper Keyser zone.

On the basis of the brachiopods, the *E. jerseyensis* Zone is correlated with the Decker Formation in New Jersey, the Rondout Formation in southeastern New York and the Cobleskill Limestone in central New York. The *M. praenuntia* Zone cannot be correlated with certainty with any other formations.

The age of the Keyser Limestone is concluded to be Late Silurian *and* Early Devonian. The *M. praenuntia* Zone contains the brachiopod genera, *Meristella,* and *Nanothyris* and the subgenus *Kozlowskiellina* (*Megakozlowskiella*) which are known only in post-Silurian rocks in other areas and suggest an Early Devonian age for the upper part of the Keyser. Halysitid corals, known only from pre-Devonian rocks, are found in the *E. jerseyensis* Zone and indicate a Late Silurian age for the lower Keyser. The boundary between the Silurian and Devonian is concluded to lie within the Keyser Limestone near the faunally and lithologically gradational boundary between the two zones.

1

INTRODUCTION

A rich, but poorly known, invertebrate fauna numbering nearly 200 species of brachiopods, ostracods, corals, bryozoans, cystoids, crinoids, pelecypods, gastropods, cephalopods, trilobites and sponges has been reported from the Keyser Limestone of Maryland and adjacent states, but few adequate taxonomic studies of any of these fossils have been made. This fauna is of special interest because of the temporal position the formation occupies in relation to the Silurian-Devonian boundary. Included among the fossils are some known only from Silurian rocks and others known only from the Devonian. In this work, the brachiopods from the Keyser Limestone within a 50 mile radius of the type section at Keyser, West Virginia, are described in detail, and the stratigraphic ranges of these brachiopods are used as criteria for investigating the position of the Silurian-Devonian boundary in eastern North America.

C. K. Swartz and others (1913), Reeside (1917), F. M. Swartz (1929) and Butts (1941), have discussed the distribution of the formation and summarized some of its gross lithologic variation from Pennsylvania to Virginia. The stratigraphic sections measured by them were found to be reliable and were used by the author with little modification. However, descriptions and illustrations of the brachiopods given by these workers are, for the most part, obsolete and inadequate.

The descriptions of the brachiopods in this work are based mainly on silicified specimens collected in large quantities from a number of horizons in the Keyser, and etched free from the calcareous matrix to expose the internal morphology. The collection is not unbiased because replacement of the brachiopods is selective in that the pseudopunctate species are not commonly silicified. In addition, most of the silicified specimens are small; complete specimens are not abundant; and the minute ornamentation is not always preserved. Hence, a smaller collection of nonsilicified specimens was made to reduce the bias from selective replacement. The erratic occurrence and selectivity of the silicification and the difficulty of extracting fossils by mechanical methods from the Keyser means that the relative abundance of specimens of different species in the collection is not a simple function of their abundance in the rocks. Expressions of relative abundance should be accepted with caution.

The vertical ranges of the brachiopods within the formation were determined from stratigraphic sections exposing either the underlying Tonoloway Limestone or the overlying New Creek Limestone, or both. All the sections studied in detail are in western Maryland and nearby parts of West Virginia and Pennsylvania within a 50 mile radius of the type section. They are located on Figure 1. Several major changes occur in the lithofacies in

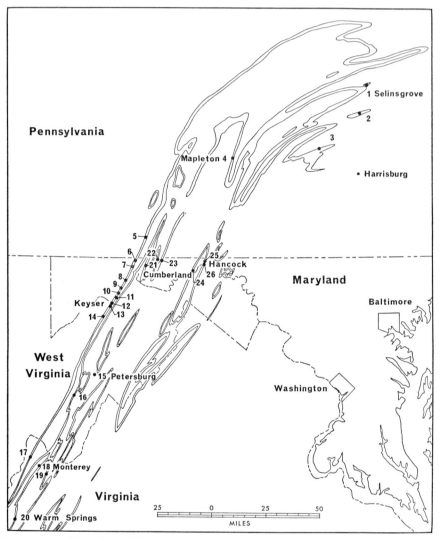

Figure 1. *Brachiopod localities.* The localities from which collections were taken are
        shown on the generalized outcrop pattern of the Keyser Limestone. Numbers
        correspond to the stratigraphic sections discussed in the text.

this area. North of New Creek, West Virginia, the formation is usually
divisible into three parts (recognized as members by F. M. Swartz, 1955):
100 to 175 feet of thin bedded, nodular, argillaceous limestone consisting
mostly of intrasparites and micrites, but also including intrasparudites,
biosparites and biomicrites, at the base; a variably bedded middle sequence
75 to 170 feet thick of argillaceous intrasparites, biosparites, biomicrites and
calcareous shales; and poorly fossiliferous, thinly laminated micrites and
biomicrites not more than 70 feet thick at the top. To the south, the
nodular layers persist, but a shale tongue, the Big Mountain Shale Member

of F. M. Swartz (1929), replaces up to 40 feet of the middle beds, and the thinly laminated beds at the top are replaced by variably bedded intrasparites.

The upper boundary of the Keyser is best exposed in the western out-crop belt between Corriganville, Maryland, and New Creek, West Virginia. Where the laminated beds are present at the top, the boundary between the Keyser and the New Creek Limestone, a massive, coarse grained crinoidal biosparite, is easily recognized on lithologic features. The contact appears conformable in this area, but in several exposures the New Creek contains limestone pebbles and fragments of stromatoporoids, corals, bryozoans and brachiopods at the base. South of New Creek, the bedding at the top of the Keyser is more variable, and the lithologic distinction between the Keyser and the New Creek is not as obvious. In all areas, the boundary can be recognized on the basis of the brachiopod fauna.

The characteristic New Creek Limestone species include:

Isorthis perelegans (Hall)
Dalejina oblata (Hall)
Schellwienella woolworthana? (Hall)
Gypidula coeymanensis Schuchert
Howellella cycloptera (Hall)
Kozlowskiellina perlamellosa? (Hall)
Uncinulus nucleolatus (Hall)

The lower boundary of the Keyser is readily recognized because the fossiliferous, nodular strata contrast sharply with the underlying, poorly fossiliferous, thinly laminated Tonoloway Limestone.

The maximum thickness of the Keyser is from 280 to 290 feet between Corriganville, Maryland, and Keyser, West Virginia. It decreases south-ward to 243 feet at Big Mountain, West Virginia, eastward to about 266 feet at Tonoloway Ridge, Maryland, and northward to less than 200 feet over most of Pennsylvania.

The following is a list of the brachiopod species described in this work:

Isorthis concinna (Hall, 1859)
Strixella sp.
Dalejina emarginata (Hall, 1859)
Resserella? sp.
Dolerorthis marylandica (Maynard, 1913)
Gypidula prognostica Maynard, 1913
Eccentricosta jerseyensis (Weller, 1900)
E. nondivergens (Swartz and Whitmore, 1956)
Schuchertella prolifica Schuchert, 1913
S. deckerensis (Weller, 1903)
Leptostrophia bipartita nearpassi (Barrett, 1878)
Strophonella (*Strophonella*) sp.
Leptaena "rhomboidalis" (Wilckens, 1769)
Merista sp. indet.
Meristella praenuntia Schuchert, 1913
Protathyris minuta (Maynard, 1913)
Nucleospira ventricosa (Hall, 1857)
Rhynchospirina martinensis n. sp.

R. newcreekensis n. sp.
Atrypa reticularis (Linné, 1758)
Cyrtina dalmani (Hall, 1857)
Kozlowskiellina (Megakozlowskiella) praenuntia (Swartz, 1929)
Howellella modesta (Hall, 1857)
H. vanuxemi (Hall, 1859)
Delthyris hyndmanensis n. sp.
Nanothyris mutabilis (Hall, 1857)
N. boucoti n. sp.
Rhynchotreta? hancockensis n. sp.
Cupularostrum litchfieldensis (Schuchert, 1903)
C. gordoni (Maynard, 1913)
C. convexorus (Maynard, 1913)
Machaeraria whittingtoni n. sp.
Boucotella gigantea (Maynard, 1913)

NEW CREEK LIMESTONE

In the region studied, the Keyser Limestone is overlain by an interval of massive or poorly bedded intrasparite less than 14 feet thick. This unit has been called the Coeymans Limestone by earlier workers because gross similarities exist between the fossils in these beds in western Maryland and the type Coeymans Limestone in New York. With their many complex facies changes and unconformities, the two units are not traceable through the intervening areas. The fossils in neither have been studied in the last 50 years. The fossils must be reexamined in both areas before their correlation can be accepted in more than a general way. Because the Maryland beds can be neither correlated with nor traced into the Coeymans of the type area, the use of the name "Coeymans" Limestone in the area from central Pennsylvania to the south should be discontinued.

A new name, the New Creek Limestone, is here proposed for these rocks. The type section is in the quarry on the north side of U.S. Route 50, one-half mile south of New Creek, in Mineral County, West Virginia (Elk Garden Quadrangle, U.S. Geological Survey Topographic Map, 15 minute series, 1943). The quarry is located 100 yards east of the stream called New Creek where U.S. Route 50 crosses New Creek Mountain. A description of the type section is given with the description of the Keyser Limestone at Locality 14. The New Creek Limestone is also exposed at: Keyser, West Virginia, Locality 12; Dawson, Maryland, Locality 10; Rawlings, Maryland, Locality 9; and Corriganville, Maryland, Locality 6.

BIOSTRATIGRAPHY

Two faunal zones, based primarily on brachiopods and coelenterates, were recognized in the Keyser Limestone in Maryland by C. K. Swartz (1913). The lower one he called the *"Chonetes"* (=*Eccentricosta*) *jerseyensis* Zone, which represented an expansion of the *"Chonetes" jerseyensis* Zone described by Weller (1903) in the Decker Formation of New Jersey. The upper zone was named the *Favosites helderbergiae praecedens* Zone. Both were recognized in later work by Reeside (1917) in Pennsylvania and F. M. Swartz (1929) in Virginia and West Virginia. The two zones were not described by these authors; instead, they were defined by a description of the "subzones" into which they were divided. Thirteen "subzones" were named in Maryland, and additional ones were proposed for the Keyser in Pennsylvania and the Virginias. Each was said to be characterized by one or more species, and they were used to correlate between Keyser exposures and with other formations. For the most part, however, they represent only similar successions of nondiagnostic faunal assemblages named on the basis of the abundant, but not always the peak, occurrence of one or more species. In most of these units, neither the species nor the assemblage is confined to the "subzone," and many species occur with equal or greater abundance at other horizons. Only a few of these "subzones" have proven useful; these were based on the peak zones of species, such as *Gypidula prognostica,* which appear to occur at the same horizon at many localities, or on species with limited ranges within the formation, such as *Rhynchospirina martinensis.* However, most of the brachiopod species range through 50 to 100 feet, or more, of the formation, and cannot be used to subdivide it into meaningful biostratigraphic units as small as these "subzones." As defined by these authors, such units do not constitute biostratigraphic subzones in the modern sense of the word; attaching names to them and using them in correlation gives a misleading impression of both the geographic and stratigraphic distribution of the fossils. It is here proposed that the "subzone" terminology used for the Keyser be discontinued. The two zones, therefore, need to be redescribed. The following descriptions are based mainly on the brachiopod species, the ranges of which are shown in Figure 2.

ECCENTRICOSTA JERSEYENSIS ZONE

The *Eccentricosta jerseyensis* Zone comprises the lower 150 to 200 feet of the Keyser Limestone in western Maryland. Its name is derived from the distinctive brachiopod, *E. jerseyensis,* which ranges from the base to approximately 150 feet above the base of the formation in most thick sections. Its greatest range occurs at Tonoloway Ridge, Locality 24, where it is

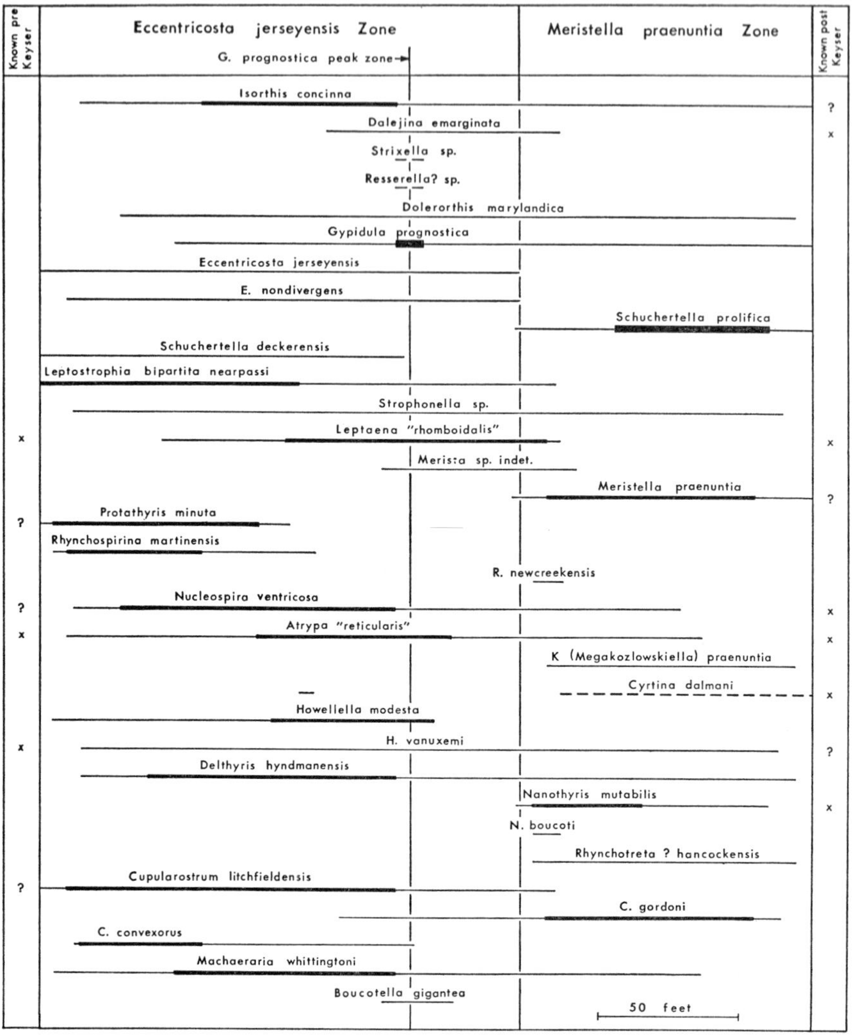

Figure 2. *Brachiopod species ranges.* The ranges of the brachiopod species within the
Keyser Limestone are shown graphically. The data from all localities are combined in one figure, using the type section as a reference standard. The scale,
in feet, is only approximate. The relative abundance of each species is indicated
by the width of the line: dashed line for very rare species; thin line, rare but
usually present; lines of double thickness, common; lines of triple thickness,
abundant. The ranges were determined by reference to the top and bottom of
the formation, and the G. *prognostica* peak zone.

found up to nearly 200 feet above the base of the Keyser. Large numbers of
specimens can be collected at only a few localities, but several specimens
can be found at nearly all of them. So far, this species has not been found
in the zone above nor in the underlying Tonoloway Limestone, and it can
be used as a reliable guide to this zone.

Gypidula prognostica is one of the most useful species in this zone. It is found infrequently in the overlying zone, especially in the sections south of Petersburg, West Virginia, but it is never abundant there. Its peak zone, or epibole, occurs in a sequence from 2 to 10 feet thick near the top of the *E. jerseyensis* Zone at nearly all localities in the area studied, and marks one of the most widely recognizable horizons in the formation. At this point it occurs in such profusion it sometimes forms a coquinite. The apparent uniqueness of this horizon in most sections makes it reasonable to assume that it is contemporaneous throughout the area, and it has been used by the writer as a reference horizon in determining the ranges of other species.

The upper limit of the *Eccentricosta jerseyensis* Zone is not sharply defined. There is no abrupt change in the lithology, and in most sections there is an intermediate sequence containing a mixed fauna lacking critical elements. The top is placed at the upper limit of the range of *E. jerseyensis* which has been found to be about 20 feet above the *Gypidula prognostica* peak zone. The typical lower Keyser species are not commonly found above this point.

The base of the zone is sharply defined because of the abrupt change from the nearly barren Tonoloway to the fossiliferous Keyser. Some of the Tonoloway species persist into the Keyser, but most of the typical Keyser brachiopods are unknown in the underlying strata.

One of the most diagnostic species in this zone is *Howellella modesta*. It is even more typical of the zone than the nominal species because it occurs in almost every section and usually in greater numbers. It has not been found in beds more than 150 feet above the base of the formation, nor in the Tonoloway Limestone below; it reaches its maximum development in the fifty feet below the *Gypidula prognostica* peak zone.

Three other common species are *Cupularostrum litchfieldensis, Rhynchospirina martinensis,* and *Protathyris minuta.* The latter two are confined to the lower 100 feet; the first species is seemingly ubiquitous in the lower 130 feet, but it also occurs sparingly in the upper zone. Since species identified as the same as these three have been reported in the Tonoloway, their precise value cannot be evaluated until the Tonoloway specimens have been restudied.

Other typical species of the zone which are locally abundant are *Delthyris hyndmanensis, Machaeraria whittingtoni, Isorthis concinna,* and *Dalejina emarginata.* The first two are new and known only from the Keyser.

Halysitid corals, including *Cystihalysites* sp., occur in this zone but have not been found in the one above. Reeside (1917, p. 190–191) reported halysitids from above the *E. jerseyensis* Zone at Tyrone and Grovania, Pennsylvania, but at each of these localities, the halysitid bearing beds belong to the upper part of the *E. jerseyensis* Zone, and the boundary between the two zones is more gradational than in other areas.

MERISTELLA PRAENUNTIA ZONE (=FAVOSITES HELDERBERGIAE PRAECEDENS ZONE OF C. K. SWARTZ, 1913)

The upper zone of the Keyser spans the top 100 to 120 feet of the formation. Its boundary with the underlying zone is not sharp, but the first appearance of its characteristic species occurs approximately 25 to 30 feet above the *G. prognostica* peak zone. *Meristella praenuntia* and *Schuchertella prolifica* are characteristic of the zone in western Maryland. Species of *Nanothyris* also appear first near the bottom of this zone, and are found in abundance at several higher horizons in a few sections. *Cupularostrum gordoni*, found sparingly in the *E. jerseyensis* Zone, is abundant and widespread in the upper zone. *Cyrtina dalmani* occurs rarely in this zone at two localities, Monterey, Virginia, Locality 18, and Big Mountain, West Virginia, Locality 16, but it is also known from a single specimen in the upper part of the *E. jerseyensis* Zone at Corriganville, Maryland, Locality 6.

Ostracods, especially species of *Leperditia, Tentaculites gyracanthus*, corals, including abundant *Favosites* sp., and stromatoporoids are common in the upper half of the zone where brachiopods are less abundant. The stromatoporoids occur in beds ranging from less than 1 to more than 5 feet thick, and in some areas, such as Corriganville, three or more beds occur in a single section. Individual beds, however, cannot be traced with certainty from one locality to another.

The upper limit of the zone is sharp, both faunally and lithologically, in western Maryland. The uppermost strata of the Keyser are sparsely fossiliferous and are overlain by the calcarenitic New Creek Limestone with a different brachiopod fauna including *Gypidula coeymanensis, Schellwienella woolworthana*, species of *Uncinulus*, and others.

C. K. Swartz (1913) named this zone the *Favosites helderbergiae* var. *praecedens* zone after the favositid coral found in abundance in it at many localities. Since characters of specific value have not been agreed upon as yet, these corals can not be identified with confidence below the generic level and the specific and subspecific names attached to them are meaningless. The genus has a long range from pre- to post-Keyser time. This name now appears to be inappropriate for the zone, and the writer considers it better to select a new name. The name *Meristella praenuntia* Zone is here proposed.

CORRELATION

Until recently, the stratigraphic units of Late Silurian and Early Devonian age from New York to Virginia were regarded as "layer-cake" formations, with boundaries that represent time planes uncomplicated by facies changes or time trangressions. Formations referred to as the "Manlius" and "Rondout" in central New York were accepted as equivalent to the units of the same names in southeastern New York and New Jersey; terms such as "Coeymans" and "New Scotland" were extended from New York as far south as Virginia and were regarded as equivalent in age to the New York rocks. It has now become apparent through more modern work (Rickard, 1962; Berdan, 1964) that facies changes are present in many of these units, and their correlation is more complex than earlier thought. That facies changes have not yet been described in these rocks south of New York state is due to a lack of modern stratigraphic work rather than to their nonexistence. Indeed, the traditional view that these formations accumulated in a shallow sea as blanketlike deposits over a relatively featureless bottom is now being questioned. Much is still to be learned of facies changes, both lithologic and faunal, and their controls in these rocks before satisfactory correlations can be made for both Keyser zones.

C. K. Swartz (1913), Reeside (1917) and F. M. Swartz (1929 and 1939) correlated the Keyser Limestone with the Decker-Whiteport-Thacher interval in New Jersey, the Rondout and Thacher of New York east of the Helderberg Mountains, and, with some reservations, with the Cobleskill, Rondout and Manlius interval in central New York.

The present data on the brachiopods supports only the correlation of the *Eccentricosta jerseyensis* Zone of the Keyser with the Decker in New Jersey, the Rondout in southeastern New York, and the Cobleskill Limestone in central New York. Correlation of the *Meristella praenuntia* Zone with other formations is inconclusive.

NEW JERSEY

Twenty-two species of brachiopods have been reported from the Decker Formation; these are listed in Table 1 along with several other common fossils. Of these, 11 are conspecific with Keyser species, and 10 of the remaining 11 will probably prove on further examination to be conspecific with, or at least closely related to, Keyser species. *Protathyris? nucleolata* has not been found by the writer in the Keyser. The species common to both formations include the most diagnostic brachiopods of the *Eccentricosta jerseyensis* Zone in Maryland. On the brachiopod evidence, the correlation of the Decker Formation with at least some part of the *Eccentricosta jerseyensis* Zone of the Keyser seems unquestionable.

11

TABLE 1. RANGES OF THE BRACHIOPODS AND SEVERAL OTHER WIDESPREAD TAXA WITHIN THE THREE ZONES OF THE DECKER FORMATION OF NEW JERSEY, FROM DATA COMPILED FROM WELLER (1903) AND SWARTZ AND WHITMORE (1956).

Brachiopoda	Zones			Present in Keyser	Similar to Keyser species
	Lower	Middle	Upper		
Craniops ovata	x		x	x	
Dalmanella? postelegantula	x	x	x		x
Rhipidomella? preoblata		x	x		x
Leptaena rhomboidalis		x	x	x	
Leptostrophia bipartita	x	x	x	x	
Schuchertella deckerensis	x	x	x	x	
Schellwienella? interstriata			x	x	
Eccentricosta jerseyensis	x	x		x	
E. nondivergens	x			x	
Sphaerirhynchia globosa			x		x
Cupularostrum litchfieldensis	x	x	x	x	
Machaeraria deckerensis	x	x			x
Rhynchonella? lamellata			x	x	
Gypidula circularis		x			x
Atrypa reticularis	x	x		x	
Howellella vanuxemi minor			x		x
Spirifer? sp. cf. H. modesta	x			x	
Cyrtina? magnaplicata	x				x
Rhynchospirina formosa?			x		x
Protathyris nucleolata			x	x	
Orthis? flabellites?	?	x			x
?Reticularia bicostata	x				x
Coelenterata					
Halysites? catenularia			x	x	
Coenites rectilineata		x	x	x	
"Cyathophyllum" inequalis			x	x	
Bryozoa					
Cyphotrypa corrugata	x	x	x	x	

The overlying beds, called the Rondout Formation by Weller (1903) and the Whiteport Member of the Rondout Formation by Rickard (1962), contain only two brachiopods: *Hyattidina? lamellosa,* unknown in the Keyser, and *Schellwienella interstriata. S. interstriata* also occurs in the lower faunal zone of the Keyser and in the Cobleskill Limestone, but this is insufficient evidence for a correlation of the Whiteport with either formation.

These beds are succeeded by the Thacher Member of the Manlius Formation which has a fauna dominated by ostracods, 22 species are described by Swartz and Whitmore (1956), but also containing a few brachiopods, corals, bryozoans and mollusks. The brachiopods are: *Mesodouvillina varistriata, Centronella? biplicata, Howellella vanuxemi, Schellwienella* sp. cf. *S. interstriata,* a rhynchonelloid and *Craniops* sp. Neither *M. varistriata* nor *C.? biplicata* is known from the Keyser. *H. vanuxemi* is a long-ranging species as it is presently understood and is not useful in this problem. The ostracods of the Manlius apparently have little in common with those of the Keyser. There is so little resemblance between the fossils in the Thacher and the underlying Whiteport in New Jersey and those in the Keyser Limestone that there is no faunal basis for correlating them.

C. K. Swartz (1913) concluded that the Rondout (Whiteport) and Manlius (Thacher) of New Jersey were approximately equivalent to the *Favosites helderbergiae* var. *praecedens* (*Meristella praenuntia*) Zone of the Keyser in Maryland on the basis of the similarity of their stratigraphic positions: both lay between the *E. jerseyensis* Zone and the "Coeymans" Limestone. Both sequences are also sparsely fossiliferous and contain stromatoporoids, tentaculitids, and ostracods. However, Swartz also pointed out that deposition of the "Coeymans" Limestone may not have been contemporaneous throughout the area from New Jersey to Maryland, and that the upper limit of the *E. jerseyensis* Zone in Maryland may not have been contemporaneous with the upper limit of the Decker Formation. Neither of these points is clarified by the present work. Whether the Whiteport-Thacher interval in New Jersey is slightly younger, equivalent to, or slightly older than the *M. praenuntia* Zone of the Keyser must remain undecided for the time being.

SOUTHEASTERN NEW YORK

Rickard (1962) correlated the Rondout Formation in southeastern New York with the Decker and "Rondout" Formation in New Jersey. Rondout fossils from New York described by Hoar and Bowen (in press) include some that are characteristic of the Decker and the lower Keyser beds and strongly suggest a correlation with the *Eccentricosta jerseyensis* Zone of Maryland. The lower three members of the Rondout, the Wilbur Limestone, the Rosendale Dolomite and the Glasco Limestone, contain the following species:

    Isorthis concinna (Hall)
    Dolerorthis marylandica? (Maynard)
    Gypidula prognostica (Maynard)
    Eccentricosta jerseyensis (Weller)
    Leptostrophia bipartita (Barrett)
    Strophonella (*Strophonella*) sp.
    Leptaena cf. *L. rhomboidalis* (Wilkins)
    Atrypa reticularis (Linné)
    Howellella modesta (Hall)
    Delthyris saffordi? (Hall)
    Cupularostrum? litchfieldensis (Schuchert)
    Lanceomyonia globosa (Weller)
    Machaeraria whittingtoni Bowen
    Machaeraria? lamellata (Hall)
    Schellwienella interstriata (Hall)
    Coenites rectilineata (Simpson)
    Cystihalysites sp.
    Cyphotrypa? corrugata (Weller)

All these fossils have been reported from the Keyser Limestone, but *Schellwienella interstriata* and *Machaeraria? lamellata* are found in abundance in the formation only in central Pennsylvania, north of the area studied. *Lancoemyonia globosa* and *Delthyris saffordi?* have not been found in the Keyser by the writer.

The Whiteport Dolomite Member at the top of the Rondout is normally a barren unit. Rickard (1962, p. 37) suggested that the "Rondout" of Weller in New Jersey correlates only with the Whiteport Member of the formation to the north.

The Thacher Limestone Member of the Manlius Formation overlying the Rondout contains a small fauna of stromatoporoids, *Tentaculites gyracanthus, Leperditia alta* and other ostracods, and *Howellella vanuxemi.* This fauna is inconclusive for purposes of correlation.

Rickard (1962, p. 108–111, and fig. 27) correlated the upper zone of the Keyser with the Coeymans and Kalkberg Limestones of eastern New York on the basis of the first appearance of terebratuloid brachiopods, in the Coeymans in New York and the upper Keyser to the south, and the presence of 22 species in common between the units. According to Rickard (1962, p. 109) these species are:

COEYMANS LIMESTONE SPECIES   KALKBERG LIMESTONE SPECIES

Brachiopoda

Strophonella? conradi   *Levenea concinna*
Leptaena "rhomboidalis"   *Leptaena "rhomboidalis"*
Meristella praenuntia   *Nucleospira ventricosa*
Atrypa "reticularis"   *Atrypa "reticularis"*
Howellella vanuxemi   *Kozlowskiellina perlamellosa*
Nanothyris mutabilis   *Cyrtina dalmani*
Uncinulus? mutabilis   *Nanothyris mutabilis*
                                     Uncinulus? nucleolatus
                                     Camarotoechia altiplicata

Pelecypoda

Megambonia aviculoides

Cephalopoda

Michelinoceras rigidum

Ostracoda

Mesomphalus hartleyi

Bryozoa

Monotrypella? arbuscula   *Orthopora rhombifera*
                                     Lioclema ponderosum

Coelenterata

Favosites helderbergiae   *Aulopora schohariae*

Porifera

                                     Hindia sphaeroidalis

The first appearance of the terebratuloids would be more convincing if the same genera and species were involved in both areas. Only one species, the variable *Nanothyris mutabilis,* is found in both areas. *Rensselaerina* is also reported from the Keyser, but not the Coeymans; and *Podolella* occurs in the Coeymans but not the Keyser. With so many different taxa involved, the first appearance of the terebratuloids lends doubtful support to the correlation.

The list of fossils cited as common to both strata seems at first to be good evidence for this correlation, but on closer examination, there is considerable room for doubt. Most of the species listed are either long-ranging, such as *Leptaena "rhomboidalis,"* or are questionably identified as conspecific, such as *Uncinulus mutabilis.* No species of *Uncinulus* have been found in the Keyser by the writer. Only the brachiopods *Nanothyris mutabilis, Nucleospira ventricosa,* and *Cyrtina dalmani,* and the ostracod *Mesomphalus hartleyi* from the Coeymans-Kalkberg Limestones are also present in and restricted to the Keyser to the south. Of these, *N. ventricosa* and *C. dalmani* are not confined to the upper Keyser but are also found in the lower zone of the Keyser. There is insufficient evidence at present to support the correlation of the Coeymans-Kalkberg Limestones in eastern New York with the *Meristella praenuntia* Zone of the Keyser.

CENTRAL NEW YORK

The thin Cobleskill Limestone contains a meager fauna consisting mainly of brachiopods and ostracods. These were studied by Berdan (1949) in a doctoral dissertation at Yale University, and she lists the following brachiopod species (Berdan, 1964, p. 15):

"Schellwienella" interstriata (Hall)
Leptostrophia bipartita (Hall)
Eccentricosta jerseyensis (Weller)
Cupularostrum litchfieldensis (Schuchert)
Machaeraria? lamellata (Hall)
Lanceomyonia? sp.
Protathyris nucleolata (Hall)
Protathyris sulcata (Vanuxem)
Howellella corallinensis (Grabau)
Howellella eriensis (Grabau)

The first five of these species occur in the *E. jerseyensis* Zone of the Keyser, and the last two, *H. corallinensis* and *H. eriensis,* cannot be distinguished by this writer from *H. modesta* found in that zone. *E. jerseyensis, L. bipartita* and *C. litchfieldensis* are among the most diagnostic species of the lower Keyser zone, and on the basis of these brachiopods and the species of *Howellella,* the Cobleskill appears to correlate with at least part of the *E. jerseyensis* Zone of the Keyser. *Lanceomyonia?* sp., *P. nucleolata* and *P. sulcata* have not been found in the Keyser by the writer. The coral *Cystihalysites* sp. also occurs in both the Cobleskill and the *E. jerseyensis* Zone of the Keyser, and indicates a Silurian age for both formations.

The Chrysler Member of the Rondout Formation overlying the Coble-skill contains a very meager fauna of *Howellella vanuxemi* and eurypterid fragments, and can not be correlated on the basis of fossils.

The members of the Manlius Formation in the western outcrop area are younger than the Thacher Member of the eastern region, and they are said to pass eastward into the Coeymans Limestone (Rickard, 1962). The fauna includes little in common with and contains none of the characteristic fossils of the Keyser Limestone.

AGE OF THE KEYSER LIMESTONE

The age of the Keyser Limestone has long been in question. It was first assigned to the Devonian (Ulrich, 1911; C. K. Swartz, 1913) because of the faunal and lithologic similarities with the overlying Helderberg limestones. It was later referred to the Silurian by F. M. Swartz (1939) because of the presence of four species derived from underlying Silurian beds; these were *"Rhynchonella" lamellata, Howellella vanuxemi, Calymene camerata* and *"Halysites" catenulatus.* More recently, Boucot (1957) suggested that the Silurian-Devonian boundary lies between the two zones of the Keyser because of the presence of *Nanothyris* in the upper zone and *"Halysites"* in the lower.

The evidence is not strong in any direction, but placing the boundary within the Keyser Limestone, between the two faunal zones, best fits present data. The ranges of 26 genera of brachiopods within the Keyser Limestone are illustrated in Figure 3. For most genera, either the ranges are too long or are not well enough known to be helpful in this problem. However, the genera *Meristella,* and *Nanothyris,* and the subgenus *Kozlowskiellina (Megakozlowskiella),* found in the Keyser only in the upper zone, are known only in Lower Devonian or younger strata in other areas of North America. *Cyrtina* also is found most abundantly in the upper Keyser zone, but one specimen has been found in the *E. jerseyensis* Zone. In other regions, this genus is confined to post-Silurian rocks. The presence of these four genera in the *Meristella praenuntia* Zone is interpreted to mean that this zone is Devonian in age.

None of the brachiopods in the lower zone is so restricted. However, the halysitid coral *Cystihalysites* is found in the lower Keyser zone, but not the upper. Halysitid corals have been reported only from pre-Devonian rocks in other areas, and they indicate that the *Eccentricosta jerseyensis* Zone is of Silurian age. The transition fauna between the two zones, which lacks these critical elements, is difficult to assign to either the Silurian or Devonian.

No widespread stratigraphic breaks have been noted within the Keyser Limestone, and the junction of the two faunal zones is never sharp. Consequently, it must be concluded that in this area, Silurian time gave way to Devonian without a marked break in either the faunal or the rock record.

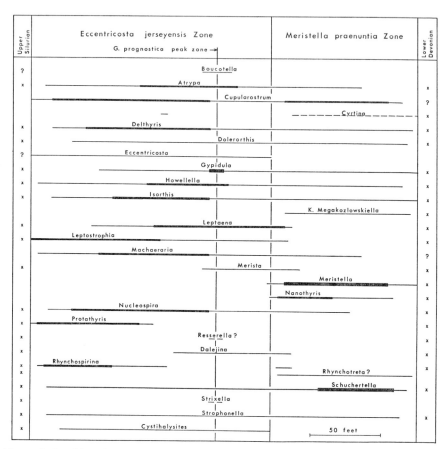

Figure 3. *Brachiopod genera ranges.* The ranges of the genera of brachiopods, listed alphabetically, and the coral, *Cystihalysites,* in the Keyser Limestone in Maryland and adjacent areas are shown with reference to the top and bottom of the formation, the boundary between the two zones, and the G. *prognostica* peak zone. The scale is only approximate.

SYSTEMATIC PALEONTOLOGY

Superfamily ENTELETACEA Waagen, 1884
Family DALMANELLIDAE Schuchert, 1913
Genus *Isorthis* Kozlowski, 1929
Type species: *Dalmanella (Isorthis) szajnochai* Kozlowski, 1929

Isorthis concinna (Hall, 1859)
(Pl. 1, figs. 1–8)

Orthis concinna HALL, 1859, p. 172, Pl. 10a, figs. 1–3
Dalmanella concinna MAYNARD, 1913, p. 301–302, Pl. 54, figs. 11–13

DESCRIPTION: Outline subquadrate, cardinal extremities rounded; biconvex in profile, pedicle valve more convex than brachial. Length about equal to width, maximum width near midlength. Pedicle beak slightly incurved, interarea apsacline, about half as wide as shell. Delthyrium open, higher than wide. A poorly defined fold extends from the umbo; in transverse section, the valve is strongly convex over the fold, but the lateral slopes are nearly flat. Brachial interarea short, less than half shell width, anacline to orthocline. Brachial beak small, often not preserved; posterolateral margins of this valve diverge at about 150 degrees. A shallow sulcus extends from the beak. Anterior commissure weakly sulcate. Surface multicostellate; costellae increase by bifurcation, 17 to 23 per 5 mm at 10 mm from beak. Surface of each valve usually marked by one or two pronounced concentric growth lines about 5 to 8 mm from the beak. Shell punctate.

Brachial interior: Brachiophores blunt, bladelike, nearly vertical, diverge from midline at 60 to 70 degrees; each supported by deposits of adventitious shell. Cardinal process small, myophore with chevron grooves on posterior face: shaft narrows anteriorly and merges with broad, low, ridge which extends to slightly beyond midlength separating the adductor scars. Fulcral plates are present. The muscle field is quadripartite with the periphery bounded by a low, discontinuous ridge: the posterior portion on each side is a continuation from the base of the brachiophore supports. The ridge is broken in about its midlength, and the anterior continuations converge toward the median ridge but do not intersect it. A low, indistinct, transverse ridge extends to the anterior ends of the posterior ridges. Each of the posterior adductor scars is bilobed. Inner peripheral surface of each valve has rounded crenulations.

Deposition of adventitious shell around the cardinalia was first on the inside of the brachiophores just anterior of the cardinal process. With continued deposition, the notothyrial cavity became more or less filled, and in extreme cases the shaft of the cardinal process appears to be wedged between thick deposits on the inner sides of the brachiophores. The brachiophores themselves may be markedly thickened and the sockets accentuated. Pallial markings not observed.

Pedicle interior: Teeth large, bluntly rounded, supported by dental plates which continue anteriorly as low but distinct ridges laterally bounding the muscle field. Accessory dental sockets border the teeth. Dental plates diverge at 50 to 60 degrees. Oblique crural fossettes present on the inner surface of the dental plates ventral to the teeth. Delthyrial cavity deep. Diductor muscle scars deep, subparallel, longer than the adductors, and bilobed at the anterior. Adductor track elevated on a broad flat to rounded ridge which separates the diductor scars. The ridge gradually increases in elevation anteriorly to about one-third shell length and then descends more rapidly to the floor of the valve. Faint adjustor impressions (?) are present on the sides of the dental plates. Pallial markings observed on only one specimen, consisting of three pairs of trunks, all originating near the anterior end of the diductor scars. One pair of trunks is laterally directed and bifurcates before reaching the margin. A second pair extends anterolaterally from the diductor scars and bifurcates at about half the distance to the anterior; at least one of the secondary trunks produced by the bifurcation also divides before reaching the margin, the others are too poorly preserved to determine. The third pair of trunks extends anteriorly from the diductor scars and is not observed to bifurcate.

DISCUSSION: The type specimens of *I. concinna* (Hall, 1859), were collected from what was called the "shaly limestone of the Lower Helderberg group: Cumberland, Maryland," (Hall, 1859, p. 172). The shaly limestone of Hall appears to be part of the Keyser Limestone. The type specimens were examined and found to differ in no way from the specimens commonly found in the lower part of the Keyser Limestone elsewhere in Maryland, Pennsylvania and West Virginia.

Dalmanella concinna (Hall, 1859) was placed in the genus *Levenea* by Schuchert and Cooper (1932, p. 123) although these authors queried this assignment. The Keyser Limestone specimens belong to the genus *Isorthis*, not *Levenea*, since all of the specimens have fulcral plates.

I. arcuaria (Hall and Clarke, 1892) from the Brownsport and Henryhouse Formations (Amsden, 1951, p. 76–77, Pl. 15, figs. 39–44; 1949, p. 44, Pl. 1, figs. 12–16) is a similar species. It may be distinguished by its more strongly biconvex profile, and relatively shorter diductor scars in the pedicle valve.

I. pygmaea (Dunbar, 1919) from the Haragan Formation (Amsden, 1958, p. 62–64, Pl. XI, figs. 5–14, Pl. XIII, fig. 24) is also similar, but it has unequal to slightly faciculate costellae, and an anacline pedicle interarea.

Dunbar distinguished *I. rockhousensis* (Dunbar, 1920, p. 122, Pl. 2, figs. 6–8) from the Keyser species by its smaller size, finer costellation, noncarinate pedicle valve and relatively small pedicle interarea.

I. propinqua (Hall, 1857, p. 110) from the middle Devonian of New York is more strongly biconvex, the brachial valve is more convex than the pedicle, and the brachial interarea is apsacline.

I. perelegans (Hall, 1857, p. 44; 1859, p. 171, Pl. 13, figs. 4–12) from the New Scotland Formation of New York is quite similar to this species, but the valves are nearly equally convex, and the costellae are more irregular.

I. szajnochai (Kozlowski, 1929, p. 75–79, text Figs. 16–18, Pl. 2, figs. 24–41) from the Silurian of Poland is more strongly biconvex, and has no sulcus; the brachial interarea is longer and nearly orthocline to apsacline, and the two posterior adductor scars are not bilobed.

I. canalicula (Schnur, 1853, p. 213, Pl. 37, figs. 5a, b) does not have smoothly rounded cardinal margins, and the hinge line is about equal to the maximum width.

OCCURRENCE: 5:116–120, 15:156–162?, 16:41–54, 59–73?, 175–185?, 198–243?, 17:15–25, 57–78?, 120–147, 22:0–93, 23:160–172?, 24:175–185, 197–211, 25:70–99.

Family RHIPIDOMELLIDAE Schuchert, 1913
Genus *Strixella* Boucot and Amsden, 1958
Type species: *Rhipidomella acutisulcata* Amsden, 1951

Strixella sp.
(Pl. 1, figs. 21–25)

DISCUSSION: A dozen small shells (5 to 6 mm in width) were found at one locality (Lantz Mountain, Virginia, 120–147 feet above the Tonoloway Limestone) which are externally like *D. emarginata* except for having a sharply defined sulcus extending from near the umbo on the brachial valve. The pedicle valve is at least as convex as the brachial, and it is flattened along the midline, but not sulcate. These cannot be juvenile specimens of *D. emarginata* because although the species is also gently sulcate at the anterior of the brachial valve, the sulcus is not present in the posterior half and is never pronounced.

Details of the external and internal surface are nearly completely obscured by the fine quartz needles with which the shells are preserved. The inner marginal crenulations are rounded. In the pedicle valve the teeth are supported by short dental plates which extend forward as ridges bounding the bilobed diductor scars separated by a low median ridge. Adductor scars and pallial sinuses not preserved. Brachial cardinalia like *D. emarginata,* but median ridge not present (or preserved).

These shells are assigned to *Strixella* Boucot and Amsden (1958) because of the distinctly sulcate brachial valve, and the subequally biconvex profile. They are too poorly preserved to warrant specific identification.

OCCURRENCE: 17:120–147.

Genus *Dalejina* Havlíček, 1953

Dalejina emarginata (Hall, 1859)
(Pl. 1, figs. 9–14)

Orthis oblata var. emarginata HALL, 1859, p. 164, Pl. XA, figs. 4–6
Rhipidomella emarginata MAYNARD, 1913, p. 302–303, Pl. LV, figs. 1–8

DESCRIPTION: Transversely oval to subtrigonal in outline; hinge line narrow, greatest width slightly anterior to midlength. Anterior margin emarginate or straight. Unequally biconvex; brachial valve more convex than the depressedconvex pedicle valve. An indistinct median depression is present in the anterior half of each valve, but is more noticeable on the pedicle valve. Pedicle beak small, slightly incurved; posterior angle 125 to 130 degrees; interarea curved, apsacline, much reduced, but longer than that of the brachial valve. Brachial beak small, suberect; interarea narrow, orthocline to apsacline. Delthyrium open, a little higher than wide. Surface multicostellate; costellae of equal size, increase by bifurcation, 18 to 24 per 5 mm at 10 mm from the beak. One or two strong concentric growth lines are usually present on each valve. Shell punctate.

Brachial interior: Brachiophores bladelike, diverging from beak at 65 to 70 degrees, supported by short brachiophore plates which are inclined posterolaterally and may be extended a short distance anterolaterally as low ridges bounding the muscle field. Dental sockets simple, expanding anterolaterally; no fulcral plates are present. Cardinal process small; posterior surface (myophore) with chevron grooves; shaft nearly perpendicular to plane of commissure, passes anteriorly into a broad ridge which divides the adductor field and extends to midlength. Adductor scars indistinct, oval, only vaguely divided into anterior and posterior pairs. Inner margins of both valves marked by peripheral crenulations which are flat in cross-section with a groove in the middle.

Pedicle interior: Teeth fairly large, supported by short plates which diverge at about 80 degrees from the beak. Dental plates convex medially and inclined posterolaterally. Umbonal cavities small. Plates continue anterolaterally as low ridges bounding the muscle field but do not reach midlength. Narrow accessory dental sockets border the teeth. Crural fossettes present but not deep. Delthyrial cavity deep; a prominent pedicle callist is present. Linear scars on the sides of the dental plates may be adjustor muscle scars. Diductor area more or less triangular, flabellate, divided by a broad to narrow median ridge which begins anterior to the delthyrial cavity and extends to midlength. Its posterior end divides the small oval adductor scars which are surrounded by the large diductor scars. Pallial markings were not observed on either valve.

DISCUSSION: Hall originally described *D. emarginata* as a variety of *D. oblata* characterized by a more extended beak, emarginate anterior and proportionally larger and more triangular pedicle diductor muscle area. The specimens described here differ only in being slightly more rounded in general than the specimens of *D. emarginata* figured by Hall. *D. emarginata* is also much smaller than *D. oblata.*

D. emarginata differs from *D. preoblata* (Weller, 1903, p. 232–233, Pl. XX, figs. 25–26) from the Decker Formation in that the latter is subcircular to subelliptical in outline, the hinge line is greater than half the width of the shell, and the anterior margin is not emarginate.

D. henryhousensis (Amsden, 1951, p. 74, Pl. 15, figs. 14–21) from the Henryhouse Formation of Oklahoma differs in being more circular in outline and in having an oval diductor area.

D. subtriangularis (Amsden, 1951, p. 75, Pl. 15, figs. 8–13) also from the Henryhouse is similar in outline to *D. emarginata* but has a larger cardinal process, and in the pedicle valve the diductor scars are not as triangular and the adductor scars do not appear to be separated by the median ridge. The anterior margin also tends to be less emarginate, and the costellae are slightly coarser.

OCCURRENCE: 5:116–120, 12:15–90, 13:15–90?, 14:23.5–31.5, 16:0–7.5?, 15–44, 73–144, 25: 70–99.

Family DALMANELLIDAE Schuchert, 1913
Genus *Resserella* Bancroft, 1928
Type species: *Orthis canalis* Sowerby, 1839

Resserella? sp.
(Pl. 1, figs. 26–33)

REMARKS: One specimen of *Resserella?* sp. was found in the middle of the Keyser Limestone, this being a silicified specimen with tiny needlelike quartz crystals obscuring the details of the external and internal surfaces. Poor preservation made it impossible to determine from this specimen the form of the cardinal process, the shape of the pedicle muscle scars, the nature of the shell substance and whether or not the teeth and sockets were crenulated.

DESCRIPTION: Subcircular outline with smoothly rounded anterior and lateral margins. Profile unequally biconvex; the pedicle valve is quite convex, but the brachial valve is nearly flat. Pedicle umbo inflated, beak slightly incurved; interarea apsacline. Posterior margin of brachial valve nearly straight, cardinal margins rounded, beak inconspicuous, interarea anacline. A faint depression is present in the brachial valve extending from near the beak and producing a gentle sinuosity in the anterior commissure. Surface ornamentation is nearly obscured by the coarse replacement by silica, but is multicostellate.

Brachial interior: Cardinal process not preserved, but the broad ridge extending anterior from it reaches to midlength dividing the more or less round adductor field. The boundaries of the quadripartite adductor scars are illdefined at their anterior. Stout, blunt brachiophores extend well into the pedicle valve. They are supported by deposits which form the posterolateral border of the adductor scars and the inner wall of the deep dental sockets. The sockets appear to be uncrenulated, but crenulations may have been obscured by the coarse silicification. Fulcral plates were not observed.

Pedicle interior: Teeth large and supported by laterally inclined, short dental plates defining small umbonal cavities; crenulatons not observed. Delthyrial cavity large and deep. Crural fossettes deep. Muscle scars not preserved.

DISCUSSION: The genus *Resserella* has had a confused history. Bancroft (1928) designated *Orthis canalis* Sowerby, 1839, as the type, but Sowerby's species was a composite of specimens from the Wenlock Shales and Caradoc Sandstone. Schuchert and Cooper (1932, p. 126) selected the Wenlock Shale specimens as the genolectotype (see Cave and Dean, 1959, p. 295), and as thus restricted, *Resserella* and *Parmorthis* (Schuchert and Cooper, 1931) are synonymous. The Ordovician specimens of *O. canalis* were assigned to another genus, *Paucicrura* Cooper, 1956, and given a new name *P. sowerbii* Cave and Dean, 1959.

Resserella is characterized by a nearly planoconvex profile, a shallow brachial sulcus and multicostate surface. In the pedicle valve, the teeth are large and crenulated, dental plates strong, delthyrial cavity and muscle scars deep, and diductor scars not strongly bilobed. The brachial interior has long stout brachiophores, crenulated sockets and an elongate-oval, quadripartite adductor field. It is principally on the planoconvex profile that this specimen is assigned to *Resserella*.

OCCURRENCE: 17:120–147.

Superfamily ORTHACEA Woodward, 1852
Family DOLERORTHIDAE Öpik, 1934
Subfamily DOLERORTHINAE Öpik, 1934
Genus *Dolerorthis* Schuchert and Cooper, 1931
Type species: *Orthis interplicata* Foerste, 1909

Dolerorthis marylandica (Maynard, 1913)
(Pl. 1, figs. 15–20)

Schuchertella marylandica MAYNARD, 1913, p. 332, Pl. 61, figs. 5–9

DESCRIPTION: Subcircular in outline; hinge line wide and straight. Pedicle interarea is long and apsacline but approaching catacline while the remainder of the valve is nearly flat or barely concave producing a subconical shell. The brachial valve is convex but only moderately so. The brachial interarea is anacline and considerably shorter than that of the other valve. The sides of the notothyrium are widely divergent producing a triangular opening, but those of the delthyrium are more nearly parallel resulting in a slitlike opening; both are unmodified by plates. The beak of the pedicle valve is poorly preserved, probably pointed and suberect. Radiating from the beak are high, abruptly rounded ribs that become larger and more widely spaced anteriorly and increase in number by unequal bifurcations. On the brachial valve 14 to 16 ribs originate at the beak, the middle three pairs of which bifurcate a short distance to the anterior giving off a smaller branch directed toward the midline in two of the three specimens studied. On the third specimen, the left half branched as the first two shells, but the right half produced the smaller branches laterally rather than medially. Further divisions occurred near the broken edges of the shells, but these were few in number and included both medial and lateral branches. Fine concentric filae ornament the interspaces between costellae. A shallow sulcus extends from near the beak of the brachial valve.

Brachial interior: Bladelike brachiophores extending as continuations of the sides of the notothyrium are supported by secondary shell deposits on each side and from beneath. A small, platelike cardinal process divides the raised notothyrial cavity at its front end but does not extend to the beak, perhaps due to imperfect preservation. The deep dental sockets have a node on their posterior walls. Anterior to the notothyrial cavity, the oval adductor scars are more deeply impressed, but distinct only at the posterior, and separated by a broad, rounded median ridge which extends to near midlength. The shell margin is corrugated, and each inner rib flattened and grooved along the middle.

Pedicle interior: Large, bluntly pointed teeth are set a bit lateral to the edge of the delthyrium; they bear a small groove on their outer edge to accommodate the socket node. Short, receding dental plates diverge from the beak and are inclined laterally, but along the floor of the valve, they continue as feeble, converging ridges outlining a weakly impressed, oval muscle area. Diductor and adductor scars cannot be differentiated. Shell margin corrugated as in brachial valve.

DISCUSSION: This species was incorrectly assigned to the genus *Schuchertella* by Maynard (1913). It is not abundant or well preserved in the Keyser. The writer found only fragmentary material from seven pedicle and four brachial valves. Maynard's types include a squashed holotype, and two poorly preserved brachial valve paratypes (USNM 53014).

This species differs from *D. fissiplica* (Roemer) from the Brownsport Formation of Tennessee (Amsden, 1949, p. 45, Pl. 1, figs. 22–25) which is planoconvex and has a more nearly hypercline brachial interarea.

D. hami Amsden (1951, p. 77, Pl. 16, figs. 1–8) from the Henryhouse Formation of Oklahoma is more uniformly biconvex and more coarsely costellate.

HOLOTYPE: USNM 53018. Keyser Limestone, Cumberland, Maryland.

OCCURRENCE: 6:16–33, 24:175–185, 240–266, 25:70–99.

Superfamily PENTAMERACEA M'Coy, 1844

Family PENTAMERIDAE M'Coy, 1844

Subfamily GYPIDULINAE Schuchert and LeVene, 1929

Genus *Gypidula* Hall, 1867

Type species: *Gypidula typicalis* Amsden, 1953

Gypidula prognostica (Maynard, 1913)

(Pl. 1, figs. 34–38; Pl. 2, figs. 1–4)

Gypidula (Sieberella) coeymanensis var. *prognostica* MAYNARD, 1913, p. 344–345, Pl. 62, figs. 9–11

Gypidula (Sieberella) coeymanensis var. *corriganensis* MAYNARD, 1913, p. 345–346, Pl. 62, figs. 12–18

DESCRIPTION: Shell subglobose; pedicle valve strongly convex, nearly semi-circular in both transverse and lateral profile; brachial valve depressedconvex, only one-third as deep as the pedicle valve. Length usually greater than width, but in some cases they are reversed. Pedicle beak incurved but not closely pressed to the brachial beak. Palintrope apsacline, grades smoothly into lateral slopes, no beak ridges present. Delthyrium as wide as high; no deltidial plates observed. Brachial beak small, pointed, suberect to incurved, interarea very narrow and short, apsacline. A weak fold is present on the anterior half of the pedicle valve and corresponding sulcus on the brachial valve; they range from fairly well defined to quite indistinct. Two or three feeble plications are present on the fold and in the sulcus, while two or more occur on each flank. The plications become obsolete both laterally and posteriorly, only rarely reaching the posterior one-third of the valve; none reaches the beak. The anterior commissure is slightly sulcate and crenulate. Weak concentric growth lines are present on both valves.

Brachial interior: The dental sockets are small notches in the anterolateral edges of the hinge plates. Cardinalia consist of three intimately joined plates which are lyre-shaped in cross-section. At the posterior, the hinge plates are convex and inclined medially; they join a pair of narrow plates concave medially which are free at their anterior tips. Supporting these are a pair of medially inclined septal plates which unite directly with the floor of the valve and extend for one-third to one-half the length. A faint median myophragm is sometimes present between weak longitudinal adductor scars. No cardinal process is present.

Pedicle interior: Teeth very small, curved posteriorly, supported by dental lamellae which converge medially to form a large spondylium (spondylium duplex) extending to nearly one-third length. The septum supports the spondylium only along the posterior third of its length but continues to midlength along the inner surface as a low but sharp ridge. Narrow, longitudinal muscle striations are present in the bottom of spondylium.

DISCUSSION: Maynard (1913, p. 344) designated this form as a variety (*prognostica*) of *Gypidula coeymanensis*. However, *G. prognostica* can easily be distinguished from *G. coeymanensis* because the latter is much larger, has a more distinct pedicle fold and more numerous and prominent plications (15 to 20), and the median plications on most specimens extend to the beak on both valves. For these reasons *G. prognostica* is raised to specific rank.

G. coeymanensis corriganensis Maynard (1913, p. 345–346) cannot be distinguished by this author from *G. prognostica*. The difference between them according to Maynard, is that *G. corriganensis* is wider than long and in some individuals the pedicle median fold is fairly well defined and "extends from a short distance anterior to the umbo to the front . . ." whereas, G. *prognostica* is longer than wide without a distinct fold or sulcus on either valve. Most of the specimens in this writer's collection are longer than wide, but a few are wider than long. In the elongate specimens there is a complete range from specimens with an indistinct fold and sulcus to specimens in which they are fairly well defined. Since there is a gradation and intermixing of the characters of the two, G. *coeymanensis corriganensis* is here synonymized with G. *prognostica*.

Two syntypes of G. *prognostica* are deposited at the U.S. National Museum. The specimen bearing number USNM 53025 is here designated as the lectotype. It is an unusually large, but otherwise typical specimen. A syntype of G. *coeymanensis corriganensis*, USNM 53031, illustrated under that name by Maynard (1913, Pl. 62, figs. 12–15), is accompanied by a handwritten note to the artist, presumably from the original author, labeling this specimen as the type of G. *coeymanensis prognostica*. This specimen is indistinguishable from specimens of G. *prognostica*. The holotype of G. *coeymanensis corriganensis*, USNM 53032, and syntypes, USNM 53041, are wide, strongly plicate specimens that fall within the range of variation of G. *prognostica*.

F. M. Swartz (1929, p. 54, Pl. 6, figs. 20–23) reported finding specimens of *Gypidula* at Monterey and Warm Springs, Virginia, in the middle of the Keyser which attain the large size of *Gypidula coeymanensis* and also have some plications that reach the beak. He recognized these as a variety of G. *coeymanensis* on the basis of the less swollen pedicle beak and fewer, broader and lower plications. The specimens found by the writer at these localities all belong to G. *prognostica*.

G. *multicostata* Dunbar (1920, p. 131, Pl. 3, figs. 12–13) from the Linden Group of Tennessee contrasts strongly with the smooth G. *prognostica* by its numerous narrow, sharp plications which extend to the beak; 10 to 12 plications are present on both the fold and sulcus.

G. *multicostata* (?) from the Haragan Formation of Oklahoma (Amsden, 1958, p. 69, Pl. 2, fig. 17) is more strongly and finely (8 costae per 10 mm) costellate than G. *prognostica*.

G. *mineolaensis* Branson (1922, p. 90, Pl. 23, figs. 6, 10, 11) from the Devonian of Missouri is ornamented by about 30 low angular costellae but lacks a fold and sulcus.

G. *simplex* Foerste (1909, p. 70, Pl. 3, figs. 51 a, b) from the Waldron of Tennessee is nearly smooth with only a few plications at the anterior edge.

G. *angulata* Weller (1903, p. 280, Pl. 28, figs. 13–21) from the upper part of the Coeymans Limestone of New Jersey has a sharply defined fold reaching to the umbo and prominent plications in the median part of the valve.

Measurements: Pedicle valves of *Gypidula prognostica* specimens from Hyndman, Pennsylvania, Locality 5, 116 to 120 feet above the Tonoloway Limestone follow:

Length	Width	Thickness	Number of plications	Length of longest plication
19 mm	18 mm	10 mm	9	10 mm
19	19	11	6?	10
22	22	13	12	15
21	20	12	12	12
18	17	10	10	15
18	16	10	7?	15
15	13	8	4?	11
17	14	10	11?	12
19	20	9	9	15
20+	20	10	10?	15
20	18	11	9?	13
15	15	9	9?	8
15	14	9	8	9
18	15	9	7	13
18	16	11	7	15

Length	Width	Thickness	Number of plications	Length of longest plication
17 mm	16 mm	10 mm	9?	15 mm
19	17	10	9?	16
19+	19	11	8?	16
16	15	8	7?	10
16+	18	9	6?	8
17	17	11	9	14
13	14	8	4?	8
17	16	10	10	12
15	15	9	9	10
18	17	9	9	15
17	15	9	9	12
16	14	9	6	13
15	15	8	6	10
15	14	9	6	10
15	15	9	7	12
17	15	10	10	13

OCCURRENCE: 1:79–93, 5:116–120, 6:16–33, 70–71, 7:53–70, 10:11–17, 12:133–135, 13:65–90, 131–134, 15:120–130, 16:59–73, 114–135, 198–243, 17:120–147, 19:57–77, 20:100–102, 21:137–140, 22:170–175, 23:162–172, 24:185–197?, 25:99–104.

Superfamily CHONETACEA Bronn, 1862
Family CHONETIDAE Bronn, 1862
Subfamily DEVONOCHONETINAE Muir-Wood, 1962
Genus *Eccentricosta* Berdan, 1963
Type species: *Chonetes jerseyensis* Weller, 1900

Eccentricosta jerseyensis (Weller, 1900)
(Pl. 2, figs. 5–6, 9–10)

Chonetes jerseyensis WELLER, 1900, p. 8; WELLER, 1903, p. 230–231, Pl. XX, figs. 12 and 15, not fig. 16; MAYNARD, 1913, p. 338–339, Pl. LXI, fig. 18, not fig. 19; SWARTZ, F. M., 1939, Pl. 2, fig. 2a-b

DESCRIPTION: Profile concavoconvex to planoconvex; width greater than length with the maximum width near midlength. Surface marked by coarse costae, 6 to 11 per 5 mm (average 8 per 5 mm) at the anterior edge. Lateral costae radiate from the hinge line, and they curve toward the anterior. Costae increase mainly by bifurcation. Six or more spines ornament the hinge line on each side of the pedicle beak, but they are preserved on only a few specimens, and only the bases of these. Those closest to the beak are directed medially, but the lateral ones are more normal to the hinge. Beak and interarea on each valve reduced and inconspicuous. Very fine concentric lines are present on well preserved specimens. Small pits on the impression of a brachial interior are interpreted as impressions of pseudopunctae. Their distribution is irregular, not radial. Size of a large specimen: length 17 mm, width 25 mm.

Brachial interior: The sessile cardinal process is bilobed with the lobes converging posteriorly. A shallow groove separates the lobes at the rear, and a central depression (alveolus of Muir-Wood, 1962) is present between the median septum and the cardinal process. The socket plates are formed by two thick, rounded ridges that buttress the cardinal process in the middle, and extend laterally roughly parallel to the hinge line. Two low, rounded ridges or septa diverge at about 30 degrees from the posterior and extend less than one-quarter shell length. An indistinct median ridge also reaches nearly to one-quarter length. Muscle scars not observed.

Pedicle interior: Stout teeth are not supported by dental plates. A short, elongate, triangular median myophragm or septum is present in the posterior. It is broad and platformlike at the rear with a shallow central groove, but tapers rapidly anteriorly and does not exceed one-third length. A pair of low ridges or septa confined to the posterior diverges at 90 degrees from the beak; they probably bordered the diductors, but no scars were discerned. A second, less distinct, pair may be present between the median and lateral ones.

DISCUSSION: This species is less abundant than *E. nondivergens* in the Keyser Limestone from which it can be distinguished by its coarser ribs which radiate more markedly from the hinge line and show a distinctive curvature toward the anterior.

"*Stropheodonta (Leptostrophia) tardifi*" var. *lambtonensis* Clark (1942, p. 24, Pl. 1, figs. 1–2) from the Lower Devonian of eastern Quebec may belong to the genus *Eccentricosta*, but it differs from *E. jerseyensis* in its straight ribs and from *E. nondivergens* in its being more coarsely costellate and in its pedicle sinus.

Eccentricosta differs from *Chonetes* Fischer de Waldheim, 1830 emended Muir-Wood, 1962 in its external ornamentation and in the form of the pedicle median septum. In *Chonetes* the septum is long, one-half to two-thirds shell length, and even though it is enlarged posteriorly, it does not form a broad, grooved triangular platform.

Protochonetes Muir-Wood (1962) has a long, broad, median septum in the brachial valve and lacks an alveolus; it also has a more transverse shell. The pedicle median septum of *Protochonetes,* however, resembles that in *Eccentricosta*. It is on the questionable basis of the similarity of the pedicle median septum that *Eccentricosta* is here placed in the subfamily DEVONOCHONETINAE Muir-Wood, 1962.

OCCURRENCE: 5:116–120, 6:59–75, 12:15–65, 135–144, 13:15–65, 24:10–45, 151–175, 185–197, 25:70–99, 104–148.

Eccentricosta nondivergens (Swartz and Whitmore, 1956)
(Pl. 2, figs. 7–8, 11–12)

Chonetes jerseyensis WELLER, 1903, Pl. XX, fig. 16; MAYNARD, 1913, Pl. LXI, fig. 19
Chonetes jerseyensis var. *nondivergens* SWARTZ and WHITMORE, 1956, p. 1090

DESCRIPTION: Profile concavoconvex or planoconvex; wider than long with greatest width near midlength. Surface ornamented by more or less straight costae numbering 9 to 14 per 5 mm at the anterior edge. The costae increase by bifurcation, rarely trifurcation and implantation. The posterolateral costae radiate from a point slightly posterior to the beak but not as noticeably as in *E. jerseyensis.* There is little or no tendency for the lateral costae to curve toward the anterior. Both beaks are small and inconspicuous. The interareas are reduced and nearly linear. The hinge line bears five or more spines on each side of the beak on the pedicle valve. Their inclination is not constant for all specimens examined. In a specimen from Big Mountain, West Virginia, Locality 16, the spines point posteromedially and slightly ventrally with the spines nearest the beak being the smallest and inclined at the lowest angle to the hinge. In a specimen from Hancock, Maryland, Locality 25, the spines are inclined laterally at a high angle. Muir-wood (1962) has emphasiezd the constancy of the inclination of spines in most chonetoid genera and species, and perhaps further study of larger collections will reveal the presence of more than one species in the Keyser Limestone. Very fine concentric lines are present especially on juvenile specimens. Brachial and pedicle interiors as in *Eccentricosta jerseyensis.* The diamond shaped median myophragm is grooved but rather high and narrow, but it probably corresponds to the wider triangular callus platform described by Berdan (1963).

DISCUSSION: Weller (1903, p. 231), in describing *E. jerseyensis,* observed all intermediate characters between small specimens with straight ribs and large ones with curved ribs. He also figured (1903, Pl. XX, fig. 16) a large specimen which had straight ribs that he identified as *E. jerseyensis.* That specimen was later designated by Swartz and Whitmore (1956, p. 1090) as the holotype of a new "variety," *E. jerseyensis* var. *nondivergens* distinguished by its nearly straight ribs.

The straight and curved ribbed specimens do not appear to intergrade in the Keyser Limestone in Maryland, and *E. nondivergens* is here elevated to specific rank. OCCURRENCE: 6:16–33, 16:73–114, 24:10–45, 25:70–148.

Superfamily DAVIDSONIACEA King, 1850
Family SCHUCHERTELLIDAE Williams, 1953
Subfamily SCHUCHERTELLINAE Williams, 1953
Genus *Schuchertella* Girty, 1904
Type species: *Streptorhynchus lens* White, 1862

Schuchertella prolifica Schuchert, 1913
(Pl. 3, figs. 1–7)

Schuchertella prolifica SCHUCHERT, 1913, p. 327, Pl. LX, figs. 1–3

DESCRIPTION: Outline semielliptical, wider than long; hinge line wide, equal to or nearly equal to the greatest width. Profile convexoconcave. Brachial valve more convex than pedicle; pedicle valve convex in umbonal region, but concave in anterior half. Cardinal margins right angles or sharply rounded. The anterolateral margin is smoothly rounded. Pedicle interarea nearly flat, apsacline, extending nearly entire shell width, several times longer than the short but wide anacline brachial interarea. Interarea bears striae parallel to the hinge line and is not observed to be divided into primary and secondary areas. Delthyrium slightly higher than wide with a convex pseudodeltidial cover. Brachial beak quite small, not extending above brachial interarea; chilidial plates very small or absent bordering the cardinal process which extends posterior to the hinge line. Ornamentation multicostate; costae increase by intercalation, 8 to 15 costae in 5 mm at the anterior. Costae high and rounded in cross-section, separated by rounded grooves. The costae are produced by corrugation of the shell so that the external grooves are ridges on the inner surface. Fine concentric lines, especially between the costae, and a few growth lines are present. No pseudopunctae were observed even in thin sections.

Brachial interior: Cardinalia prominent; cardinal process of moderate size, bilobed with each lobe also divided into two. Anterior surface of the process is nearly perpendicular to the plane of the commissure; its quadrilobed posterior surface is irregular and nodular. A low, broad, rounded median elevation extends for a short distance anteriorly from the cardinal process. The muscle scars are weakly impressed, occupying a small area in the posterior quarter of the shell. Their shape can not be discerned. The cardinal process is buttressed by a pair of crural plates which diverge from the posterior at 80 to 90 degrees. The plates are curved, strongly convex anteromedially, and join with the floor of the valve to form one side of each of the dental sockets which expand anterolaterally. Each plate terminates in a bluntly rounded point.

Pedicle interior: Large, blunt teeth are not supported by dental plates. The traces of the teeth along the sides of the delthyrium are thickened but not united with the floor of the valve. Muscle area indistinct, not deeply impressed; a small pair of elongate-oval adductor scars separated by a small median rise is present just anterior to the delthyrial cavity. No median septum is present.

DISCUSSION: The genus *Schuchertella* was proposed by Girty (1904) for orthotetacids which lack a median septum and lack extended dental plates in the pedicle valve, and in which the socket walls (crural plates) are not extended so as to partially surround the muscles in the brachial valve. The profile, however, is variable among species of *Schuchertella*. Some authors (Weller, 1914, p. 53–54; Dunbar and Condra, 1932, p. 117; Stehli, 1954, p. 298) have specified that the profile is planoconvex or biconvex. Thomas (1910, p. 93–94), on the other hand, indicated that a convexoconcave profile also occurs; and Cooper (1944, p. 343) states that the profile is "occasionally biconvex but usually with ventral valve concave or with less depth than dorsal. . . ."

Schuchertella most closely resembles the genus *Schellwienella* Thomas, but they are distinguished by most authors mainly on the presence of dental plates in *Schellwienella*.

However, Weller (1914, p. 59) placed more emphasis on the resupinate profile than on the presence of dental lamellae in distinguishing *Schellwienella* from *Schuchertella*. He noted that there is variation in the strength of development of dental plates in the specimens of *Schellwienella* which he examined, and in some the dental plates are little or no different from those of *Schuchertella*. If this interpretation were followed, *Schuchertella prolifica* could perhaps be placed in the genus *Schellwienella* on the basis of its profile, but to the present writer it seems better and more in agreement with other workers to place greater weight on the absence of dental lamellae until this problem has been more thoroughly studied.

In defining this species, Schuchert (1913, p. 327) states that it is similar to *Schellwienella woolworthana* (Hall), which he assigned to the genus *Schuchertella*, from the Coeymans Limestone, and that there are transitional forms which often make the separation of the two species difficult or arbitrary. He did not point out that *Schuchertella prolifica* lacks dental lamellae, whereas *Schellwienella woolworthana* has dental lamellae in the Maryland specimens examined by the writer (and, therefore, belongs to the genus *Schellwienella* Thomas).

Amsden (1958, p. 91) has pointed out that there is some question about the pedicle interior of *Schellwienella woolworthana* (Hall, 1857). He noted that in specimens from the New Scotland Formation of New York, some possessed dental lamellae, while in others they were receding and poorly developed. He states, "There is some question whether this indicated that the development of the plates is not a constant feature, or whether there may be two species included under this one name."

The variation in *Schellwienella woolworthana* from the Maryland Helderberg is unknown because the description given by Schuchert is quoted from Hall (1859), and the only two pedicle interiors figured are from the New Scotland Formation of New York after Hall (1861, Pl. 17, figs. 11 and 2b).

Until a restudy is made of *Schellwienella woolworthana* (Hall), it must be assumed that this species at least has receding and poorly developed dental plates, and thus, may be distinguished from the Keyser species, *Schuchertella prolifica*.

Schuchertella haraganensis Amsden (1958, p. 88–90, Pl. XI, figs. 1–4; Pl. XIII, firs. 18–20) from the Haragan Formation of Oklahoma is a similar species especially with its convex brachial valve, but it differs from *S. prolifica* in having the greatest width at the hinge line, the cardinal extremities angular to slightly extended, and in having a more pronounced median ridge in the brachial valve.

S. attenuata (Amsden, 1951, p. 84–85, Pl. 17, figs. 9–14, and 1958, p. 152–153, Pl. XIV, figs. 26–31), from the Henryhouse Formation of Oklahoma appears to be even more similar to *S. prolifica;* however, the profile of *S. attenuata* is biconvex with the brachial valve weakly convex and the pedicle valve with a slightly greater convexity. The brachial interarea is also longer than that on *S. prolifica*.

OCCURRENCE: 10:4.5–9.5, 12:223–230, 14:57–71, 24:218–230, 240–266.

Schuchertella deckerensis (Weller, 1903)

(Pl. 2, figs. 17–21)

Orthothetes deckerensis WELLER, 1903, p. 229, Pl. 20, figs. 6–7
Schuchertella deckerensis MAYNARD, 1913, p. 329, Pl. 60, figs. 13–16

DESCRIPTION: Outline subelliptical, wider than long. The hinge line is straight and slightly less than the maximum width which is near the midlength. Only rarely is the hinge line slightly extended. Profile biconvex, but the pedicle umbonal area is somewhat conical, whereas the anterolateral slopes are flat or concave. The brachial valve is markedly convex. The pedicle interarea is high and flat, divided into primary and secondary areas, apsacline to nearly catacline. The brachial interarea is linear or absent. Delthyrium higher than wide, covered by a convex pseudodeltidium. The beak may be slightly hooked or not. The pedicle valve is asymmetrical in all of the specimens observed; most commonly the beak is twisted and the halves of the interarea are unequal. Surface multicostellate with high and not closely spaced costellae, some of which are tubular and open at irregular points near the anterior margin. At the anterior, the costellae are merely corrugations of the shell, approximately 12 to 14 occurring in 5 mm. A few concentric growth lines are usually present. No pseudopunctae were observed, but since only silicified specimens were found, they may be absent due to lack of preservation.

Brachial interior: Cardinal process bilobed, with each lobe also divided into two on the posterior face (myophore). Cardinal process joined laterally to thin, strongly curved crural plates which unite with the posterior margin and form the anterior wall of the dental sockets. The sockets are simple and expand laterally. Muscle scars are not impressed. No distinct median elevation is present. The inner surface is smooth in posterocentral part because of secondary deposits, but there is a wide marginal corrugated zone.

Pedicle interior: Teeth small and blunt, not supported by dental plates. A thickened ridge marks the trace of each tooth along the margin of the delthyrium, but these ridges do not unite with the floor of the valve. Muscle scars too feebly impressed to discern. Inner surface is the same as in the brachial valve.

DISCUSSION: Only small and intermediate size individuals of this species were collected by the writer, but they are conspecific with Maynard's (1913, Pl. 60, figs. 13–16) hypotype specimens (USNM 53023a,b,c) identified as *S. deckerensis* (Weller). They differ from Weller's (1903, p. 229–230, Pl. 20, figs. 6–7) species only in lacking the coarse wrinkles and large attachment area on the pedicle valve, and in having a higher interarea.

This species differs from *Schuchertella sinuata* (Hall and Clarke, 1892, Pl. 20, figs. 8–9) from the Helderberg? Group at Cumberland, Maryland, in that it lacks a well defined sulcus in the brachial valve.

S. deformis (Hall, 1857 and 1859, p. 174, Pl. XA, fig. 12; Pl. XV, fig. 3) from the New Scotland Formation of New York differs from this species in being longer than wide; the pedicle valve is more convex than the bracial; the hinge line is only three-fourths the width of the shell; and the interarea is "sometimes nearly on a plane with the axis of the shell."

The internal structures of these two species are not known. Comparison with other species is difficult at present because the structures of the interiors are so poorly known that one is not certain that the older species are actually members of the genus *Schuchertella.*

An area of attachment was not seen on any of the specimens of the pedicle valve of this species, but almost all specimens were poorly preserved in the area of the beak. Perhaps a cicatrix of attachment was originally present but not preserved. The asymmetrical pedicle valve is irregular in most cases, as if it had been attached to the substrate.

OCCURRENCE: 5:116–120, 6:59-75, 8:0–56, 13:15–90, 16:0–7.5, 21:21–45, 22:0–93, 25:70–99.

Superfamily STROPHOMENACEA King, 1846
Family STROPHEODONTIDAE Caster, 1939
Genus *Leptostrophia* Hall and Clarke, 1892
Type species: *Strophodonta magnifica* Hall, 1857

Leptostrophia bipartita nearpassi (Barrett, 1878)
(Pl. 3, figs. 8–10; Pl. 4, figs. 1–2)

Strophodonta nearpassi BARRETT, 1878, p. 372
Stropheodonta bipartita WELLER, 1903, p. 226, Pl. 20, figs. 1–5
Stropheodonta (Leptostrophia) bipartita MAYNARD, 1913, p. 316, Pl. 57, figs. 17–18
Stropheodonta (Leptostrophia) bipartita var. *nearpassi* PROUTY and SWARTZ, 1923, p. 426,
  Pl. 18, fig. 4

DESCRIPTION: Outline transversely semi-elliptical, the greatest width at the straight hinge line. Profile planoconvex or nearly so; the pedicle valve is not strongly convex. Pedicle interarea apsacline, twice as high as the anacline brachial interarea. Delthyrium closed, at least in part, by a small convex pseudodeltidium that is only rarely preserved. Notothyrium and chilidium not observed. Radial ornamentation consists of fine costellae which curve gently posteriorly near the lateral margins. The costellae are widely spaced near the margin, sometimes with implanted smaller ones between them. The pseudopunctae are arranged in radial rows in the interspaces between the costellae. Fine, closely spaced, concentric filae are present over the entire surface and curve at the ends of the hinge line in such a way as to indicate that mucronate extensions were present.

Brachial interior: Small, but stout, bilobed cardinal process with flat, striated, posteroventrally facing myophores. Bordering each lobe there is a nodelike plate at the posterior, presumably representing the much reduced socket plates. Extending forward along the midline is a low, broad ridge bisecting the adductor area and reaching beyond midlength. The adductor scars are elongate-oval, not marked at their anterior, but deeply impressed at the posterior. The hinge line is denticulate over most, if not all, of its length.

Pedicle interior: Large triangular diductor scars are bounded by straight lateral ridges diverging from the beak at 70 to 90 degrees and bisected by the anterior continuation of the ventral process as a low median ridge. Process pits deep in some specimens. Adductor impressions, separated by the median ridge, are oval and much elongated, but not deeply impressed. Low radiating myophragms divide the large diductor field. The posterolateral surface of the shell is tuberculate, but the muscle areas are smooth.

DISCUSSION: This subspecies is the same as the species described by Barrett (1878, p. 372) and Weller (1903, p. 226) from the Decker Formation of New Jersey. It also occurs in the Tonoloway Limestone (Prouty and Swartz, 1923, p. 426). It is distinguished from *L. bipartita bipartita* (Hall) from the "Coralline" Limestone by its curved ribs versus straight ones in the latter. Barrett's species, *L. nearpassi* was placed in synonymy with *L. bipartita* (Hall) by Weller (1903, p. 226) and reduced to a "variety" of Hall's species by Prouty and Swartz (1923, p. 426). Since the specimens in the Keyser of Maryland differ from those from New York in the character of rib curvature, it is advantageous to recognize the Maryland form as a subspecies of *L. bipartita.* If greater importance is placed on the curvature of the costellae in the future, it may be desirable to re-elevate *nearpassi* to specific rank.

This form differs from *L. becki tennesseensis* Dunbar, 1920, from the Haragan and Bois d' Arc formations of Oklahoma (Amsden, 1958, p. 78, Pl. 3, figs. 15–20, Pl. 6, fig. 1, Pl. 11, figs. 27–28) in lacking the undulating rugae, in being more finely costellate, and in having wide spaces between the costellae. They are otherwise similar and both have curved costellae.

OCCURRENCE: 2:40–55, 3:64–94, 5:116–120, 8:0–7.5, 11:30–37, 12:0–133, 13:0–133, 15:13–51, 21:56–87, 24:10–45, 185–197, 25:70–99.

Genus *Strophonella* Hall, 1879

Type species: *Stropheodonta semifasciata* Hall, 1863

Strophonella (Strophonella) sp.
(Pl. 2, figs. 13–16)

DESCRIPTION: Outline transversely semi-elliptical, width greater than length, greatest width at the straight hinge line. Profile convexoconcave, resupinate: the pedicle valve is gently convex in the posterior one-third, becoming markedly concave toward the front and sides. The brachial valve is nearly flat in its posterior part and parallel to the pedicle valve elsewhere. The flat pedicle interarea is apsacline, longer than the anacline brachial interarea. Both beaks are small and inconspicuous. The apical portion of the delthyrium is covered by a convex pseudodeltidium. Notothyrium and chilidium not preserved. Surface ornamentation consists of fine, sharp, radial costellae (10 to 14 per 5 mm at 15 mm from beak) which are widely spaced, the interspaces being at least twice as wide as the ribs, and increase by implantation and bifurcation (?). The pseudopunctae are arranged in radial rows in the grooves between the ribs, usually two rows per groove. Weak concentric growth lines occur at irregular intervals.

Brachial interior: None is preserved.

Pedicle interior: Hinge line denticulate for one-half of its length. No dental plates are present, but the pseudodeltidium is buttressed by a stout ventral process which has two short, thick, lateral branches defining the posterior edges of the adductor scars. The process continues for a short distance anteriorly as a low, median myophragm separating the elongate-oval adductor scars; a median groove is present in the ridge at the posterior edge of the adductor scars. The large, flabellate diductor field is bounded by a distinct raised lobate ridge extending to near midlength. Small myophragms corresponding to the edges of the lobes are present. The remainder of the inner surface is papillose because of projecting radial pseudopunctae.

DISCUSSION: Although no brachial interiors of this species were collected, the finely preserved pedicle valves illustrate the generic characters (see Williams, 1953, p. 48) of *Strophonella*. They have a concave pedicle valve with partially denticulate hinge line, pseudodeltidium supported by a ventral process, diductor field surrounded by a raised, "petaloid" ridge, and wide oval adductor scars. These specimens are assigned to the subgenus *S. (Strophonella)* because of the lack of dental plates and the presence of a fairly well developed pseudodeltidium.

Their specific assignment is uncertain, but they are of the type of S. *punctulifera* (Conrad, 1838) and *S. cavumbona* (Hall, 1857) from the Helderberg Group of New York. The difference, if any, between these two species is vague and Schuchert (1913, p. 323) and also Hall and Clarke (1892, p. 291) have placed them in synonymy.

This may have been the Keyser Limestone form named *S. keyserensis* by Swartz (1913, p. 324), but the characters of that species are nearly unknown since it is illustrated by only one poor figure and the description is short and undiagnostic.

Strophonella punctulifera described by Weller (1903, p. 277, Pl. 27, figs. 6–7) from the Coeymans Limestone of New Jersey appears similar, but the geniculation is more abrupt than in the Keyser species.

Strophonella (Strophonella) bransoni Amsden (1958, p. 70, Pl. 4, figs. 15–21) from the Haragan Formation is more triangular in outline and more coarsely costellate (7 per 5 mm) than this form.

S. (S.) sp. figured by Williams (1953, Pl. 13, fig. 13) from the Birdsong Shale is identical in internal form to this species.

Compared with *S. geniculata* (Hall, 1859, p. 483, Pl. 23, figs. 6a-c) from the Helderberg? Group at Cumberland, Maryland, the Keyser shells are more gently geniculate and lack a pedicle fold and brachial sinus.

S. leavenworthana (Hall, 1857, p. 53; 1859, p. 189, Pl. 21, figs. 5–7; Pl. 23, figs. 1–3) from the New Scotland Formation of New York may be distinguished because it is ornamented by concentric wrinkles on the central disk.

OCCURRENCE: 4:18–27, 14:57–71, 24:240–266.

Family LEPTAENIDAE Hall and Clarke, 1894
Genus *Leptaena* Dalman, 1828
Type species: *Leptaena rugosa* Dalman, 1828

Leptaena sp. cf. L. *"rhomboidalis"* (Wilckens, 1769)
(Pl. 4, figs. 3–5)

DESCRIPTION: Outline subquadrate to semicircular; greatest width at the straight and extended hinge line. Width always greater than length, rarely approaching twice as wide as long; dimensions of an average size specimen: length 19 mm, width 25 mm. Profile concavoconvex with brachial valve weakly concave to the lateral and anterior margins where it bends abruptly away from the pedicle valve into a long trail. Pedicle valve convex in the central area and geniculate at the margin. Both beaks are small and obscure;

a round apical foramen seen on only a few specimens. Interareas nearly linear, pedicle apsacline, brachial anacline. Surface ornamented by fine, radiating costellae (12 to 16 per 5 mm at front edge just posterior to the geniculation) which cross 10 to 15 concentric wrinkles in the valve. The wrinkles are small at the posterior, but from about 1 cm anterior to the beak to the trail the wrinkles are pronounced features. On abraded specimens these 7 to 10 large corrugations may be the only ones preserved. The shell is pseudopunctate with the pseudopunctae arranged in radial rows in the grooves between the costellae.

Brachial interior: Stout, sessile, bilobed cardinal process with flat posterior faces; each lobe is supported by a callus swelling which bifurcates to form low ridges. The median branches join in front of the cardinal process, then continue anteriorly as a low thin ridge bisecting the muscle field. The adductor scars are small, oval depressions on each side of the ridge which extends to just beyond midlength. The dental sockets are long, shallow grooves diverging between the cardinal process and the hinge line.

Pedicle interior: Teeth supported by dental plates; each plate continues forward as a curved ridge bounding the oval muscle field which is halved by a low, rounded, median ridge.

DISCUSSION: These specimens appear to differ in no significant way from the long ranging, widely distributed *Leptaena "rhomboidalis."*

OCCURRENCE: 1:80–102, 3:40–95, 5:116–120, 7:94–108, 24:185–218, 25:104–148.

Superfamily ATHYRIDACEA, M'Coy, 1844
Family MERISTELLIDAE Waagen, 1883
Subfamily MERISTINAE Hall and Clarke, 1895
Genus *Merista* Suess, *in* Davidson, 1851
Type species: *Terebratula herculea* Barrande, 1847

Merista sp. indet.
(Pl. 4, figs. 6–9)

DESCRIPTION

Pedicle exterior: Valve convex, outline oval, subcircular to elongate. All specimens collected are incomplete with the anterior and lateral edges broken off. Surface smooth with no indication of a sulcus. The umbonal slopes are somewhat angular; the beak suberect, apex not preserved. Delthyrium large, nearly as wide as high. No deltidial plates preserved. Palintrope concaved posterolaterally.

Measurements of two large, but incomplete specimens; length 21 mm, width 21 mm, and length 21 mm and width 16 mm.

Pedicle interior: Delthyrial cavity large and deep, bounded by short dental plates which diverge from the posterior at up to 60 degrees, but in many they become nearly parallel anteriorly. The plates slope medially and vary from weakly concave to weakly convex toward the midline; they are extended anteriorly as low ridges. In several large shells the shallow umbonal cavities are filled, obscuring the dental lamellae. A transverse, inclined, arched septum or plate ("shoe-lifter process" of earlier authors) extends from the delthyrial cavity to midlength or beyond. Posteriorly, the plunging crest of the "shoe-lifter" extends nearly to the beak in some, while in others it ends at the anterior edge of the delthyrial cavity. In most specimens it is gently arched, but in several the crest is sharply rounded or angular. The width of the "shoe-lifter" at its anterior edge varies from one-third to one-half the shell width. The ridges extending from the dental lamellae in most of the specimens run onto the flanks of the "shoe-lifter" before expiring, but in some the ridges are parallel to the edges of the "shoe-lifter" and a deep, linear groove separates them.

Brachial valve unknown.

DISCUSSION: The "shoe-lifter" process in the pedicle valve is a diagnostic feature of *Merista.* The only similar genus is the Devonian *Dicamara* Hall and Clarke, 1894, which presumably is similar to *Merista* in pedicle interior. It differs in having an arched septum in the brachial valve and in the area under the shoe-lifter being divided into two compartments by the brachial median septum.

The Keyser specimens show the following variations: (1) outline subcircular to elongate, (2) umbonal cavities present or absent, (3) "shoe-lifter" wide to narrow, rounded to angular, and (4) extended dental ridges parallel to or running onto the "shoe-lifter." Hall (1859, p. 487) recognized two species of *Merista* (=*Camarium*), *M. typa* and *M. elongata* from Cumberland, Maryland, probably from the Keyser Limestone. According to Hall, in *M. typa* the ridges extending from the dental lamellae run onto the "shoe-lifter," whereas in *M. elongata* the ridges are parallel to the edges of the "shoe-lifter" and do not run onto it. In addition, the "shoe-lifter" was described as proportionally longer and narrower in *M. elongata,* and the shell more elongate in outline. These characters are mixed in the Keyser specimens collected by the writer, and are also mixed in Hall's syntype specimens in the American Museum of Natural History. The specimens at hand are not well preserved and do not warrent specific identification, but most of them agree in form with *M. typa.* Hall and Clarke (1894, p. 71) referred to *M. elongata* as a probable variety of *M. typa,* and Schuchert (1913, p. 449) placed the two species in synonymy.

OCCURRENCE: 16:114–135, 17:120–147, 19:57–67, 20:100–102, 23:163–173, 24:214–218.

Subfamily MERISTELLINAE Waagen, 1883
Genus *Meristella* Hall, 1859
Type species: *Atrypa laevis* Vanuxem, 1842

Meristella praenuntia Schuchert, 1913
(Pl. 4, figs. 10–22)

Meristella praenuntia SCHUCHERT, 1913, p. 443, Pl. 73, figs. 43–46, Pl. 74, figs. 1–4

DESCRIPTION: Outline subpentagonal to suboval; length greater than width especially in juveniles; maximum width at or slightly anterior to midlength. Strongly biconvex profile, the pedicle valve being the deeper. Pedicle beak large, erect to incurved, arched over brachial beak; terminating the beak is a large rounded foramen isolated by small, coalesced, deltidial plates (see Pl. 4, figs. 18 and 21). Indistinct beak ridges bound the slightly posteriorly facing curved palintropes. The small pointed brachial beak is erect to incurved and fits snugly into the lower part of the delthyrium beneath the other beak. A brachial fold and pedicle sulcus are present, but often poorly developed in the posterior half; their development varies from feeble to pronounced. The fold is sometimes flattened or weakly depressed along the crest. Anterior commissure rectimarginate to moderately uniplicate. Surface smooth except for irregularly spaced growth lines.

Brachial interior: Median septum high and narrow, extending to near midlength; at its posterior end it divides to form a broad, Y-shaped septalium which narrows toward the beak. The hinge plates and the "branches" of the septum meet abruptly to form sharp ridges which continue into the crural bases, but no covering plate is present. The hinge plates are concave longitudinally. The sockets are narrow, deeply set and partially enclosed by the overlapping edges of the hinge plates. Muscle scars feebly impressed, elongate-oval, not distinctly divided into anterior and posterior adductor pairs. Anterior and lateral surfaces marked by numerous closely spaced grooves of the pallial sinuses on a few specimens, but not as pronounced as in the pedicle valve. The spires have 8 to 12 turns on each side with the apices directly laterally. Jugum points posteroventrally and terminates in a pair of scissor shaped loops above the point of junction of the basal branches (see Figs. 4 and 5).

Pedicle interior: Teeth of moderate size, curved at their ends toward the posterior-midline. Short dental plates support the teeth, but the plates may be obscured by secondary deposition in mature shells. Anterior to the large delthyrial cavity is a deeply impressed triangular diductor scar. A narrow groove that may represent the adductor track joins the two depressions. The diductor scar is longitudinally striated and poorly defined at the anterior but extends to midlength or beyond. The remainder of the interior surface is marked by shallow radial grooves of the pallial sinuses. Both valves are thickened

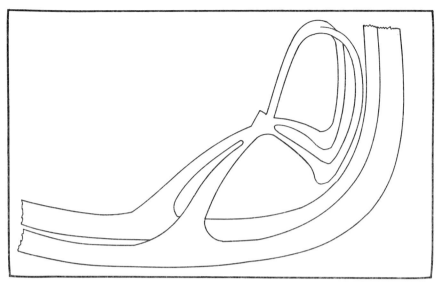

Figure 4. *Lateral view of jugum of* Meristella praenuntia. Note the scissorslike loops. The jugum points toward the pedicle beak. The posterior is to the right.

in the umbonal region by secondary shell material in larger specimens, but deposition is far greater in the pedicle valve.

DISCUSSION: The genus *Meristella* as used here is based on *Atrypa laevis* Vanuxem, 1842 as the type species. There has been some confusion about the type species of the genus, and the problem has been summarized by Amsden (1958, p. 129–130).

The genus *Meristina* Hall, 1867 is similar in most respects to *Meristella* and can be distinguished only with difficulty by the nature of the jugum and the dental plates. In *Meristella* the jugum bears a pair of loops beyond the point of juncture of the basal branches, while *Meristina* has only a very short bifurcation. The dental plates in *Meristella* are characteristically short, whereas those in *Meristina* are long (Boucot, personal communication, 1962).

A dozen partially complete juga were found; in most, the scissorlike loops were broken,

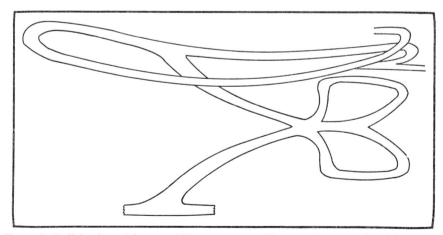

Figure 5. *Pedicle view of jugum of* M. praenuntia. The posterior is to the right.

leaving either a pair of laterally directed rods on each side, or only one pair of lateral rods plus the longitudinal extention of the central part. No *Meristina*-type juga were found although some of the broken juga resemble the simple bifurcating termination of *Meristina*. The various broken juga look like intermediate steps in the development of the looped *Meristella* jugum from the simpler *Meristina*, but since all of the specimens appear to be broken, it is questionable if any but the *Meristella*-type are represented.

M. praenuntia is similar to *M. arcuata* (Hall, 1857, p. 95, Figs. 1–4) from the New Scotland Formation of New York, but the latter is larger, more transverse and has a more pronounced sulcus.

M. wisniowskii Kozlowski (1929, p. 219, Pl. 11, figs. 36–41) from Poland is quite similar to this species but has a much more pronounced pedicle sulcus.

OCCURRENCE: 9:66.5–75, 10:4.5–9.5, 12:170–187, 212–230, 14:17–23.5, 57–71, 24:228:–266, 26:0–41.

Family ATHYRIDIDAE M'Coy, 1844
Genus *Protathyris* Kozlowski, 1929
Type species: *Protathyris praecursor* Kozlowski, 1929

Protathyris minuta (Maynard, 1913)
(Pl. 5, figs. 1–6)

Whitfieldella minuta MAYNARD, 1913, p. 442, Pl. 73, figs. 41–42

DESCRIPTION: Small, elongate shells attaining a maximum length of about 5 mm and width of 3.5 to 4 mm; meristelloid in shape, truncate at the front. Biconvex profile with the valves nearly equally convex, both a little more convex in the umbonal region. Pedicle beak pointed, erect to a little incurved, elevated above brachial. Delthyrium narrow, no plates were observed; a small, round apical foramen is present. Brachial beak small, inconspicuous, suberect. The medial part of the pedicle valve is flat or faintly depressed into a sulcus. The brachial valve is also flattened medially but to a lesser degree. Anterior commissure weakly uniplicate or rectimarginate. Surface smooth except for feeble concentric growth lines near the margin, none of these are lamellose.

Brachial interior: The inner wall of each laterally expanding dental socket is strongly convex toward the midline. Attached to them are the hinge plates which are inclined toward the middle and join at their anterior ends forming a concave, spoon shaped platform between the socket walls with a perforation at the posterior. No median septum is present. The crural bases project anteriorly from the plates. Only two juga were found, neither is complete. Jugum Y-shaped with a long central branch that is broken at the end, but appears to have been bifurcate at the tip. Muscle scars lightly impressed, but a faint pair of elongate-oval impressions occur on either side of the midline about halfway between the beak and midlength.

Pedicle interior: Teeth supported by short, delicate dental plates bordering narrow umbonal cavities. Muscle impressions are barely discernible; a faint pair of oval depressions near the front of the delthyrial cavity can sometimes be detected (=adductor scars?). The diductor scars occupy a vague, elongate area beginning in the delthyrial cavity and reaching nearly midlength.

DISCUSSION: *Protathyris* Kozlowski (1929, p. 223) has a complex jugum, but lacks a saddle; the basal branches join into a median rod directed toward the crural points, which bifurcates into two long, curved, accessory lamellae running parallel to the primary lamellae in their posterior loop, but ending before the primary lamellae curve anteriorly. In the Keyser species, *P. minuta*, the complete jugum is not known, but it probably bifurcated at its distal end.

Buchanathyris Talent (1956, p. 36) also has a perforate, free hinge plate, but this plate is convex rather than concave, and the jugum is simple with only a short posterior pointing median apophysis.

Hindella (?) (*Greenfieldia*) *congregata* Swartz (1923, p. 459, Pl. 25, figs. 10–22) from the

Tonoloway Formation of Maryland and West Virginia has an unsupported and undivided cardinal plate similar to that in *P. minuta*, but the brachial valve has a median fold often bearing a narrow sinus, and on the inside there is a low myophragm. Swartz (p. 461) also named two varieties of this species. All three are larger than, but quite similar to, *P. minuta;* they are undoubtedly congeneric.

OCCURRENCE: 8:0–56, 12:0–65, 13:0–65, 21:21–45, 22:0–93, 25:36–48.

Family NUCLEOSPIRIDAE Davidson, 1881
Genus *Nucleospira* Hall, 1859
Type species: *Spirifer ventricosa* Hall, 1857

Nucleospira ventricosa (Hall, 1857)
(Pl. 5, figs. 16–27)

Spirifer ventricosa HALL, 1857, p. 57, not figs. 1 and 2
Nucleospira ventricosa HALL, 1859, p. 220–221, Pl. 14, figs. 1a–h, Pl. 28B, figs. 2–9; HALL and CLARKE, 1894, Pl. 48, figs. 2–6, 18; WELLER, 1903, p. 290, Pl. 30, figs. 19–22; SCHUCHERT, 1913, p. 430, Pl. 73, figs. 10–12

DESCRIPTION: Outline transversely oval. Profile biconvex with the valves subequally convex, the pedicle is slightly deeper. An indistinct median depression on each valve can usually be detected, but it is never pronounced and in some only a vague flattening is present. The anterior commissure is rectimarginate. Faint, sparse growth lines are the only surface ornamentation preserved. Beaks on each valve approximately erect, that of the brachial valve curves under the other and fits into the delthyrium. The pedicle beak extends only a short distance posterior to the brachial beak. Delthyrium wider than high, closed by a concave plate which fills the apical half.

Brachial interior: Large, prominent cardinal process projects ventrally from the bottom of the valve into the cavity of the pedicle valve and bends abruptly to the posterior. Its distal end fits into the delthyrial cavity. The ventral face of the process is concave (seat of the diductor muscles). The vertical anterior face is divided by a longitudinal groove which may be concealed by secondary shell deposits. The crural bases are attached at the point where the cardinal process curves sharply to the posterior. Spires laterally directed, ten or more turns on each side. Jugum not preserved. The lateral edges of the base of the cardinal process are supported by thickened calluses. The sockets are directed somewhat to the posterior because the inner wall is formed by the curved cardinal process. A low, median ridge extends from the base of the cardinal process to the anterior. At the anterior, it loses its sharpness of definition; and at the posterior it may expand to form a buttress at the base of the cardinal process. Adductor scars consist of two main pairs of longitudinal impressions divided by the median ridge; a broad, rounded myophragm which narrows anterolaterally separates the pair on each side of the septum.

Secondary deposits of shell material are common in large specimens, frequently on the ventral face of the cardinal process, filling the concave depression and concealing the longitudinal groove. The muscle scars and myophragms are accentuated by the deposits, but the median ridge may be replaced by a groove by greater deposition around rather than on it.

Pedicle interior: Teeth stout, smoothly rounded into hooks; dental plates absent, but each tooth is supported by a thickened base. Well developed secondary sockets border each tooth. A low, median septum extends from the beak to the anterior edge, but it is usually concealed in the delthyrial cavity by secondary shell deposits, and at the anterior edge it becomes broader and less distinct. Muscle scars are feebly impressed, but secondary shell material may accentuate them. Adductor scars are oval, separated by the median septum and located just anterior to the delthyrial cavity. Their anterior margin is not well defined. Bordering the adductor scars laterally and anteriorly is a large flabellate diductor area which is marked by radial lobes, six or more per side, separated by low, rounded myophragms. The diductor scars extend to midlength.

DISCUSSION: Most of the species of *Nucleospira* have been based on variations in the distinctness of the sulci, convexity of the valves, ratio of the length to width, presence of growth lines, and shell size; but the differences between species are nearly always vague. In the collection from the Keyser Limestone, all these characters are variable, and the validity of some of the reported species is questionable. Some specimens look like *N. swartzi*, and others resemble *N. elegans*; considered together, they seem to represent variations within the species *N. ventricosa*. No species are placed in synonymy here because the range of variation within each and at each locality and within each horizon is unknown, but the following are some of the species which are quite similar and differ little from each other.

N. elegans Hall (1859, p. 222, Pl. 28B, figs. 10–14) from the New Scotland Limestone is larger and more transverse than *N. ventricosa*, and the brachial sinus is broad at the anterior producing a gently sulcate commissure.

N. pisiformis Hall (1859, Pl. 28B, figs. 1a–d;=*Orthis pisum*, Hall, 1852, p. 250, Pl. 52, figs. 1a–e) from the Niagara Group of New York is a small, more or less circular form in which the brachial valve is more convex than the pedicle.

N. concinna (Hall, 1843, p. 200, Fig. 3; and Hall and Clarke, 1894, Pl. 48, figs. 12–17, 19–34) from the Middle Devonian of New York is quite similar to *N. ventricosa*, and the features which separate the two are unclear.

N. rotundata Whitfield (1882, p. 194) from the Upper Silurian of Ohio is elongate and strongly rotund.

N. swartzi Maynard (1913, p. 432, Pl. 73, figs. 15–17) from the Keyser Limestone is larger and less globose than *N. ventricosa*, and the pedicle valve is much more convex than the brachial valve.

N. robusta Kozlowski (1929, p. 216–218, Pl. XI, figs. 24–35) from Poland has a short but nearly straight hinge line, the convexity of the valves is equal, and the pedicle beak is not much elevated above that of the brachial valve.

N. raritas Amsden (1958, p. 157) from the Brownsport and Henryhouse Formations is a small, circular to elongate form.

The four species described by Weller (1914, p. 453–458), *N. rowleyi* Weller, *N. barrisi* White, *N. minima* Weller, and *N. obesa* Rowley, from the Mississippian differ from *N. ventricosa* mainly in being smaller and less transverse, and *N. barrisi* has a low brachial fold. These four species differ only slightly from each other, but each is found at a different horizon.

OCCURRENCE: 5:116–120, 6:16–33, 59–75, 10:11–17, 11:37–62, 12:65–133, 13:0–15?, 65–90, 14:17–23.5, 16:59–73, 185–198, 21:59–87, 25:70–99.

Superfamily RETZIACEA Waagen, 1883
Family RHYNCHOSPIRINIDAE Schuchert and LeVene, 1929
Genus *Rhynchospirina* Schuchert and LeVene, 1929
Type species: *Waldheimia formosa* Hall, 1857

Rhynchospirina martinensis n. sp.
(Pl. 5, figs. 9–15)

Rhynchospira globosa SCHUCHERT, 1913, p. 425–426 (not Hall, 1857)

DESCRIPTION: Outline subpentagonal; posterolateral margins diverge at about 95 degrees, slightly concave, extending to near midlength; anterior margin rounded to nearly straight. Width a little greater than length in most specimens. Valves subequally convex; profile tends to be subglobose. Pedicle beak incurved or erect, small and pointed, elevated and arched over the brachial beak; the apex of the beak is not perforated by the foramen. Instead, the foramen is hypothyrid, never mesothyrid; along its dorsal margin, it is bordered by conjunct deltidial plates. The apex of the delthyrium is closed by a small deposit leaving only a circular opening for the pedicle. Surface marked by 12 to 19 (average 16) angular plications. The median portion of each valve is weakly depressed into a sulcus, that on the pedicle valve being greater. The pedicle sulcus is occupied by two, infrequently three, much smaller plications which disappear before reaching the beak. The midportion of the brachial valve is raised into a broad, barely noticeable fold, the midpart of which is depressed into a weak sulcus. The commissure is crenulate and faintly uniplicate. Weak zigzag growth lines are present near the front. Shell punctate.

Brachial interior: The large, fourlobed cardinal plate projects ventrally beyond the plane of contact of the two valves. The posterior pair of lobes extends beyond the hinge line into the delthyrial cavity of the pedicle valve. The anterior lobes are notably concave on their ventral surfaces: they continue anteriorly into the crural bases. The cardinal plate is supported by a strong septum which extends to near midlength. Laterally, the cardinal plate is supported by a pair of posterolaterally curving plates which form the inner walls of the moderately small dental sockets. Muscle impressions consist of an indistinct oval depression on each side of the median septum. Secondary shell deposits in larger specimens thicken the supports of the cardinal plate and partially smooth out the plications.

Pedicle interior: Teeth bluntly rounded, supported only by their curved, thickened bases which extend obliquely inward and anteriorly from the margin of the delthyrium. No dental plates are present. Delthyrial cavity large and usually coated by a secondary deposit of shell material. No pedicle tube present. Muscle scars feebly impressed in the grooves produced by plication of the valve.

Measurements:

| | | | Number of Plications | | | |
| | | | Pedicle | | Brachial | |
Length	Width	Thickness	Valve	Sulcus	Valve	Sulcus
10.0 mm	10.4 mm	8.2 mm	16	3	17	2
8.5	9.1	5.3	14	3	15	2
8.3	8.1	5.0	16	2	15	1
7.9	8.4	5.3	16	2	15	1
7.7	7.6	4.6	17	3	17	2
7.6	7.7	5.0	16	2	15	2
6.1	6.3	3.5	18	2	18	2
5.9	6.0	3.4	16	2	16	2
4.0	4.1	2.1	16	2	16	2
3.3	3.4	2.0	14	2	12	?

DISCUSSION: These Keyser specimens differ in only one respect from typical *Rhynchospirina:* the foramen is hypothyrid and does not impinge on the beak. The taxonomic value of this character is unclear. Specimens are frequently broken at the tip of the delicate beak, and many workers have been vague in describing the beak region. It is here given specific value. Davidson (1867, p. 127) noted a similar difference in British Wenlock Shale species which he assigned to *Retzia salteri,* and ranked the hypothyrid forms as a variety (*bayleyi*). Later raised to specific rank, *R. bayleyi* was also reported by Kozlowski (1929, p. 212, Pl. 9, figs. 25–26) from Poland, where it is also characterized by an imperforate beak. Only closer attention to the position of the foramen in the future will determine its significance. The species name is derived from Martin Mountain, Locality 22, its type locality.

Compared with *R. globosa* (Hall, 1857, p. 87) from the New Scotland of New York, the Keyser specimens differ only in the position of the foramen. In Hall's species the foramen pierces the beak. Schuchert (1913, p. 425, Pl. 72, figs. 16–22) identified the Keyser specimens as *R. globosa.* Schuchert's figures (Pl. 72, figs. 20–22) showing a mesothyrid foramen are inaccurate for lower Keyser specimens.

R. formosa (Hall, 1857, p. 88) from the New Scotland Formation of New York may be distinguished by the position of the foramen and by having fewer plications.

R. rectirostra (Hall, 1857, p. 89) from the Oriskany Sandstone of Maryland is easily distinguished by its straight beak, low posterior angle (45 degrees) and triangular outline.

R. formosa (Hall) of Weller (1903, p. 240, Pl. 21, figs. 30–34) from the Decker Formation of New Jersey is probably the same as *R. globosa*. It has 16 to 18 plications and a prominent, incurved beak; but Weller did not describe the foramen, and his figures are inconclusive. It, therefore, cannot be compared with the Keyser specimens.

R. formosa, of Weller (1903, p. 289, Pl. 31, figs. 9–11) from the Coeymans Limestone is larger and more finely plicated than *R. martinensis*, and is probably the same as Hall's species, *R. formosa*.

Amsden (1949) assigned three Brownsport Formation species to *Homeospira*, but only one brachial interior was illustrated, that of *H. elongata*. In it, the cardinal plate lacks the posterior extensions found in *Rhynchospirina*, but also absent is the small, linear cardinal process of *Homeospira*. The pedicle valve of that species has conjunct deltidial plates, unlike typical *Homeospira*. The distinction between these two genera is unclear, and the generic assignment of this species is at least open to question. The assignment of other rhynchospirinid species to *Homeospira* raises similar questions (Amsden, 1958, p. 140–141), and a thorough reexamination of the type species of *Homeospira* is now needed. The brachial interiors are unknown for the other two species. All three are easily distinguished from the Keyser species. *H.?* *elongata* Foerste (Amsden, 1949, p. 67, Pl. 10, figs. 16–23) has a mesothyrid foramen. *H.?* *schucherti* Foerste (Amsden, 1949, p. 67, Pl. 10, figs. 6–10) has a mesothyrid foramen, and the beak is not incurved and arched over the brachial beak. *H.?* *beecheri* Foerste (Amsden, 1949, p. 68, Pl. 10, figs. 11–15) is smaller and has fewer plications (12 to 14) than *R. martinensis*, and it has a mesothyrid foramen.

Rhynchospira? *attenuate* Stewart (1922, p. 248, Pl. 65, fig. 3) from the Little Saline Limestone of Missouri has fewer plications (10 to 12) and a more acute posterior angle than *Rhynchospirina martinensis*.

Trematospira acadiae Hall (1860, p. 146, Fig. 4)=*R. salteri* var. *acadiae* (McLearn, 1924, p. 85, Pl. 10, figs. 1–7) from the Moydart and Stonehouse Formations of Nova Scotia is quite similar to the Keyser species; they have about the same number of plications; but the foramen and internal structures are unknown. (Hall's figure shows much straighter posterolateral sides than McLearn's.) Its generic assignment is unverified.

R. sinuata Hall (1860, p. 146; McLearn, 1924, p. 86, Pl. 10, figs. 18–19) from the Stonehouse is larger, has more plications (17 to 22) and is more elongate than *R. martinensis;* it resembles *R. formosa*.

R. excavata Grabau (1903, p. 1050, fig. 9) from the Manlius (?) of New York resembles *R. formosa* but is characterized by excavated, concave, posterolateral sides. The beak is incurved but broken; foramen and interior structures unknown.

R. praeformosa Grabau (1910, p. 131, Pl. 20, figs. 2–3; Pl. 30, figs. 15–16) resembles *R. formosa*, but the mesial depression on the brachial valve has a single, smaller, median plication that extends to the beak flanked by two others that do not reach the beak. In the pedicle sulcus a single median plication splits at about one-third the valve length.

Retzia? *haidingeri* (Barrande, 1879, Pl. 32, figs. 13–29) lacks the characteristic depression of the smaller, median plications into a sulcus on each valve.

R.? *bayleyi* from Poland (Kozlowski, 1929, p. 212, Pl. 9, figs. 25–26) has only 13 or 14 plications and a small pedicle "pseudo-area."

R.? *siemiradzkii* Kozlowski (1929, p. 214, Pl. 9, figs. 27–34) is characterized by a perforate beak (permesothyrid foramen).

HOLOTYPE: MCZ 9467a. Pl. 5, fig. 13.

PARATYPES: MCZ 9467b, 9466a, b.

TYPE LOCALITY: Martin Mountain, Maryland, Locality 22, Keyser Limestone, lower 93 feet.

OCCURRENCE: 3:0–25, 4:0–38, 6:16–33, 12:15–65, 13:15–65, 21:0–17, 21–45, 22:0–93, 24:10–45, 25:70–99.

Rhynchospirina newcreekensis n .sp.
(Pl. 5, figs. 7–8)

DESCRIPTION: This species is like *R. martinensis* in outline and profile but differs in the ribbing and the pedicle beak structure. Both valves are marked by a subdued central depression less well developed than in *R. martinensis*. Each depression bears a pair of smaller ribs at the anterior, but on the pedicle valve they are derived from the bifurcation of a median rib which disappears before reaching the beak; on the brachial valve, the two ribs are generally present all the way to the beak. On some specimens a central rib is intercalated near the anterior between the reduced median pair. There are 12 to 17 ribs present on each valve, but the average is 14, fewer than in *R. martinensis*. The pedicle beak is suberect to erect, truncated by a mesothyrid to permesothyrid foramen. The delthyrium is completely closed by deltidial plates.

Brachial and pedicle interiors: Details of the internal structure are unknown, but both anterior and posterior extensions of the cardinal plate are present.

DISCUSSION: This species is distinguished by the number of plications, the manner in which the central ribs are added and the suberect, foramenate beak. It most closely resembles *Homeospira? elongata* Foerste (Amsden, 1949, p. 67, Pl. 10, figs. 16–23) and *R. siemiradzkii* Kozlowski (1929, p. 214, Pl. 9, figs. 27–34); it is distinguished from both by the pattern of the central ribs.

The specific name is derived from the type locality at New Creek, West Virginia, Locality 14.

HOLOTYPE: MCZ 9465. Pl. 5, fig. 7–8.

TYPE LOCALITY: New Creek, West Virginia, Locality 14, Keyser Limestone, unit 2.

OCCURRENCE: 14:17–23.5.

Superfamily ATRYPACEA Gill, 1871
Family ATRYPIDAE Gill, 1871
Subfamily ATRYPINAE Gill, 1871
Genus *Atrypa* Dalman, 1828
Type species: *Anomia reticularis* Linné, 1758

Atrypa reticularis (Linné, 1758)
(Pl. 5, figs. 28–40, Pl. 6, figs. 1–5)

Anomia reticularis LINNÉ, 1758, p. 702, no. 195 excl. Mus. Tess. Pl. 5, fig. 5
Atrypa reticularis ALEXANDER, 1949, p. 208 (contains a revision with the selection and description of a lectotype)

DESCRIPTION: Outline subcircular, elongately oval to subtriangular; specimens that are wider than long are about equal in number to those having the length greater than the width. Greatest width is between the middle and the posterior. Profile markedly unequally biconvex in large specimens; the brachial is much more convex than the pedicle valve which is depressed convex or convex only in the umbonal region and concave at the lateral and anterior margins. Brachial valve much inflated giving a strongly arched longitudinal and transverse profile. Pedicle beak suberect to erect, closely curved over but extending only slightly posterior to the brachial beak which is also suberect. No delthyrial modifications seen. A narrow brachial fold and pedicle sulcus are variably developed but usually present on large specimens in the anterior third of the shell producing a moderately uniplicate commissure. Surface ornamented by rounded costellae, numbering four to six per 5 mm at 15 mm anterior to the beak, which increase by bifurcation, some as many as four times between the beak and the margin. Concentric growth lamellae cross both the costellae and the interspaces, and on well preserved specimens the lamellae flare to form "spines." The lamellae are more closely spaced and more prominent near the anterior.

Brachial interior: Cardinalia consists of curved socket walls joined to the crura to form narrow hinge plates with inner and outer lobes. Sockets are large and bear a transversely grooved, longitudinal ridge. Little or no secondary deposit is found in the notothyrial cavity in most specimens, but in some, a massive deposit completely fills the space between the socket wall (see Pl. 5, fig. 34). There is a complete gradation between specimens with no deposit at all and those with a massive structure. In typical development, the anterior face of the deposit is vertical, and the ventral face is nearly parallel to the plane of contact of the valves. A deep longitudinal groove bisects the ventral face: it was presumably the seat of the diductor muscles. On one specimen, a trilobed cardinal process is mounted on top of the deposit (see Pl. 5, figs. 33, 35). In shells without the notothyrial deposit, the muscle scars are not deeply impressed and cannot be divided into adductor pairs. In deposit bearing shells, a low median ridge bisects the circular adductor field. Surrounding the adductor scars is a strongly pitted "genital" area. The spiralium consists of at least 12 turns in each cone; the apices of the cones are directed toward the middle of the brachial valve. Jugum not observed.

Pedicle interior: The large, blunt teeth are joined to the lateral margins of the shell and supported by very short dental plates which may be completely hidden by later shell deposition in large specimens. According to the generic diagnosis of *Atrypa* given by Alexander (1949, p. 208) no true dental lamellae are present in members of this genus; instead the teeth are supported by pedestal-like processes. The specimens at hand, however, have plates supporting the teeth and defining umbonal cavities which the writer cannot distinguish from true dental plates. Bounding the teeth posterolaterally are two well developed secondary dental sockets. The ends of the teeth are notched by a shallow groove. The delthyrial cavity is broad but shallow; the apex is filled with a pedicle callist. At the front of the delthyrial cavity a short, longitudinal or two elongate-oval depressions mark the seats of the adductor muscles. Laterally from these and beneath the teeth are a pair of large, triangular scars (see Pl. 5, fig. 32) which can be seen only in specimens with secondary deposits thickening the shell. In large specimens with extensive deposition of secondary material, the diductor field is large, circular, and bounded by a marked callus ridge which is lower at the anterior end. Bordering the ridge is a strongly pitted area. The width of the diductor field is equal to or greater than half the valve width, and it may extend to midlength. The scars are longitudinally striated with numerous low, rounded, bifurcating myophragms.

Measurements: Specimens from Hancock, Maryland, Locality 25, 104 to 148 feet above the Tonoloway Limestone, follow:

Length	Width	Thickness	Number of plications per 5 mm at 15 mm from beak on pedicle valve	Fold and sulcus present
16.7 mm	15.6 mm	8.0 mm	4	x
18.5	19+	10.5	5	weak
21.1	20.9	12.8	6	x
21.5	25.0	11.7	5	x
21.5	18+	12.5	6	weak
22.0	20.5+	11.5	5	x
23.0	24.0	14.0	4	x
23.2	22.9	12.0	5	x
23.6	25.0	13.0	5	x
24.5	22.0	16.0	6	x
25.5	24.0	16.5	6	x
26.6	27.3	13.5	4	x

Discussion: *Atrypa reticularis* has been reported previously from the Keyser Limestone by many workers who based their identification on the external characters of the shells, but the internal structures have not been described. More than 600 specimen of this species were collected from the formation and examined by the writer; 200 specimens are silicified shells which show the structures of the brachial cardinalia. Externally, these shells are similar and possess the typical features of *Atrypa reticularis*. Internally, they are not all alike. Some have the cardinalia typically found in this species. Others have a massive deposit completely filling the notothyrial cavity. Such a structure has not been reported previously in the genus *Atrypa;* and it is difficult taxonomically to reconcile these specimens with normal specimens of *Atrypa reticularis*. However, because there is a complete gradation among shells in the Keyser Limestone from specimens with no deposit to ones with a massive deposit, these shells do not appear to represent two different taxa. They are all here identified as *A. reticularis*.

Specimens bearing the massive deposit are not found in every bed in the Keyser containing *A. reticularis*. They have been found at only two localities in the Keyser Limestone and at one New Creek Limestone locality. The normal shells are found at many localities, most commonly in fine-grained, argillaceous carbonates which suggest a nonturbulent environment of deposition. In these beds, few or no deposit bearing shells are found; none have a massive deposit. Shells containing a massive deposit are found in coarse-grained calcarenites and calcareous, silty shales which suggest a turbulent environment. Few normal shells are found in these rocks. In rocks suggesting an environment of intermediate turbulence, such as fine-grained, argillaceous calcarenites, all stages in the development of the deposit are found.

Because of the complete range in the development of this deposit shown by these shells and the apparent association of the deposit bearing shells with rocks indicating a turbulent environment of deposition, the deposit is interpreted as an intraspecific adaptation in *A. reticularis* to increase the weight and stability of the shell for life in a turbulent environment.

It is also possible that this is a gerontic feature developed on normal *Atrypa cardinalia*, but the presence of large numbers of these shells at only a few localities, and the occurrence of larger specimens without the brachial deposit in other Keyser localities do not support this.

If the environmental interpretation is correct, then the brachial cardinalia in this group of shells is not a conservative feature and should be used with caution in superspecific classification.

A deposit similar to that seen in the Keyser shells is partially developed in *A. reticularis* (Hall, 1859, Pl. 42, fig. 1m) from the New Scotland of New York.

A. tennesseensis Amsden (1949, Pl. 9, fig. 9) from the Brownsport Formation seems to show the initial stage in the development of such a deposit.

The original description of *Atrypa reticularis*, and even the revision by Alexander (1949, p. 208), allows a wide range of forms to be placed in this species. A great many Silurian and Devonian specimens have been assigned, and, although some stratigraphic variation has been noted (Hall and Clarke, 1894, p. 168; Kozlowski, 1929; Alexander, 1949), little has been done to bring out the details of this variation. The relative taxonomic importance of the many different characters, such as profile, relative convexity of the valves, outline, development of fold and sulcus, rib number and branching pattern, growth lamellae, size and strength of muscle scars, and so on, has never been determined. Indeed, it is only the rare description that even mentions all these features, so it is difficult to compare different descriptions of *A. "reticularis"* satisfactorily. The following are only a few of those that could be mentioned.

The general form is similar to that illustrated by Hall (1859, Pl. 42), and Hall and Clarke (1894, Pl. 55, figs. 1–17) from the Helderberg Group of New York.

There is a noticeable similarity between the Keyser specimens and the Late Silurian subspecies of *A. reticularis* recognized by Alexander (1949) from the Great Britain; but there are differences (in size, relative convexity of the valves and development of the fold and sulcus) between Keyser specimens and the Early Silurian subspecies of Alexander.

Similar differences are found between the Keyser shells and the Clinton specimens of Hall (1852, p. 72, Pl. 23, fig. 8).

A. reticularis var. *dzwinogrodensis* Kozlowski (1929, p. 170–173, Pl. 8, figs. 1–7) from the Silurian of Poland is also a similar type, but Kozlowski's other two "varieties" (*tajnensis* and *nieczlawiensis*) are more finely ribbed.

The Keyser specimens are similar to *A. tennesseensis* Amsden (1949, p. 62, Pl. 9, figs. 1–9) from the Brownsport Formation of Tennessee but are more variable and have a more pronounced fold and sulcus. They differ from *A. oklahomensis* Amsden (1958, p. 116, Pl. 9, figs. 24–35, Pl. 12, figs. 34–35) from the Haragan Formation of Oklahoma in not having the fold so strongly developed.

Occurrence: *Normal shells:* 5:30–48.5, 116–120, 6:16–33, 11:37–62, 12:90–133, 135–144, 13:15–134, 16:44–73, 21:59–87, 96–140, 24:185–197, 211–214, 25:99–148.

Deposit-bearing shells: 17:20–70, 120–147, 24:214–218. New Creek Limestone, 10:0–10.

Superfamily Suessiacea Waagen, 1883
Family Cyrtinidae Frederiks, 1912
Genus *Cyrtina* Davidson, 1858
Type species: *Calceola heteroclita* Defrance, 1827

Cyrtina dalmani (Hall, 1857)
(Pl. 6, figs. 9–20)

Cyrtina dalmani Hall, 1857, p. 64; Hall, 1859, p. 206, Pl. 24, figs. 2a–y; Swartz, 1929, p. 57, Pl. 7, figs. 4–7.

Description: Shell small, very unequally biconvex; width always greater than length, maximum width at hinge line or just to the anterior; the cardinal margins are slightly extended or rounded. Pedicle valve pyramidal; interarea high, width nearly equal to valve width, strongly apsacline to nearly catacline. Beak only weakly curved, nearly straight. Delthyrium high and narrow, covered by a convex plate which forms a short tubular border around an oval shaped foramen. Brachial valve semicircular, depressed convex, nearly flat; beak small and inconspicuous, nearly straight to suberect. Brachial interarea linear. Anterior commissure uniplicate and crenulate. The pedicle valve bears a median sulcus with a rounded cross-section which begins at the beak and expands anteriorly and projects into the brachial fold. There are three or four lateral plications on each side of the sulcus which decrease in size toward the posterolateral border. The brachial valve bears a median fold which is broad and rounded or gently flattened in cross-section. There are two or three plications on each side of the fold. Several specimens have the pedicle beak twisted so that the valves are not symmetrical, and the plications may be unevenly developed on the two sides of the valve. Concentric growth lines are present on most specimens and some appear to bear very fine, closely spaced striae or spines, but all specimens are silicified and details of the surface ornamentation are not well preserved. Punctae not preserved.

Brachial interior: Cardinal process small and bilobed, but may be enlarged by secondary shell deposits. Process in some shells notched by thin, longitudinal grooves representing the diductor scars, especially on the posterior face. Crural plates well developed, diverge from the beak but are inclined toward the midline. They join the posteromedian part of the shell in a callus under the cardinal process and do not extend forward along the bottom of the valve. The lateral margins of the crural plates form the inner wall of the large, divergent, dental sockets. A pair of narrow, longitudinally elongate muscle impressions separated by a feeble myophragm occurs in the deep trough produced by the brachial median fold. The crura extend nearly straight forward for about one-third of the valve length before bifurcating to form the jugum and primary lamellae. The spires and the jugum were not observed.

Pedicle interior: Teeth blunt, not much curved, nearly straight extensions of the thickened delthyrial margins. Well developed dental plates join the median septum at about half the distance between the teeth and the bottom of the valve to form a "spondylium." The median septum extends along the floor of the "spondylium" as a hollow tube, the tichorhinum, which reaches to the beak. The tube is bisected inside by a thin septum which is present only along the top and bottom of the tube. Although the incomplete division of the tube by this septum appears to be due to the original structure, it may be due to incomplete preservation. The distinction can not be made in this case, but it may be of taxonomic importance (Amsden, 1963, p. 126). The tube and median septum extend a short distance anteriorly beyond the point where the dental lamellae depart. The median septum continues along the floor of the valve to from one-fourth to one-half the valve length. No muscle scars were seen.

Measurements: Four unmeasured brachial valves had seven plications each; p.v. indicates that only the pedicle valve was measured. Listing of measurements follows:

Length	Width	Thickness	Number of Plications Pedicle	Brachial
7.3 mm	10.0 mm	6.0 mm	7	7
6.5	8.4	5.5 p.v.	8	...
5.5	8.4	5.6	8	...
3.3	5.6	3.2 p.v.	8	...
4.3	5.0	2.6	6	5
3.1	5.0	3.7	6	7
2.2	3.9	2.0 p.v.	6	...
2.1	3.5	1.8 p.v.	6	...
4.3	8.0	3.9	6	5
5.5	8.8	4.0 p.v.	10?	...
5.9	7.2	4.5	6	5
4.4	6.2	4.0	6	6

DISCUSSION: This form differs in no important way from *C. dalmani nana* Amsden (1958, p. 133, Pl. 7, figs. 19–28) from the Haragan Formation which was distinguished from *C. dalmani dalmani* from the New Scotland Formation of New York by its smaller size. The Keyser specimens are about the same size as those from Oklahoma, but since there are so few specimens (only 36, most of which are incomplete), they are not assigned to either subspecies.

C. dalmani described by Tansey (1922, p. 200, Pl. 51, figs. 30–31, Pl. 52, figs. 1–4) from the Bailey Limestone of Missouri appears to be the same as this species and Amsden's subspecies.

C. pyramidalis (Hall, 1852, p. 266, Pl. 54, figs. 7a–e) from the Middle Silurian of New York has a greater number of lateral ribs, five per side, than *C. dalmani*.

C. praecedens Kozlowski (1929, p. 207, Pl. 11, figs. 8–23) from Poland differs from *C. dalmani* from the Keyser only in having a greater number of ribs on most specimens, a higher maximum number of ribs and a greater maximum size.

OCCURRENCE: 6:16–33, 16:135–156, 185–198, 18:110–130?

Superfamily DELTHYRIDACEA Phillips, 1841
Family DELTHYRIDAE Phillips, 1841
Subfamily KOZLOWSKIELLININAE Boucot, 1962
Genus *Kozlowskiellina* Boucot, 1958
Subgenus *Megakozlowskiella* Boucot, 1957
Type species: *Spirifer perlamellosus* Hall, 1857

Kozlowskiellina (Megakozlowskiella) praenuntia (Swartz, 1929)
(Pl. 6, figs. 6–8)

Spirifer perlamellosus var. *praenuntius* SWARTZ, 1929, p. 56, pl. 7, figs. 18–20

DESCRIPTION: Shell transverse, greatest width at or near the hinge line. Biconvex in lateral profile with the pedicle valve much deeper than the brachial. Pedicle interarea weakly curved, several times longer than that of the opposite valve; both interareas are apsacline. Pedicle beak slightly hooked, suberect; brachial beak small and inconspicuous. Plates modifying the narrow delthyrium not preserved. Surface ornamented by coarse, radial plications crossed by prominent, frilly, growth lamellae over the entire surface, 8 to 10 in 5 mm. A broad, median fold on the brachial valve begins at the beak; it is round to slightly flattened in cross-section and twice as wide as the neighboring plications. Three to five plications diminishing in size laterally occur on each side; these are not as elevated as the median fold. A broad, median sulcus is present on the pedicle valve. Fine, radial ornamentation appears to be present but because the shells are silicified, it is preserved only in a few spots. Anterior commissure uniplicate and crenulate. Most of the specimens are between 10 and 15 mm wide, but the largest is a crushed and incomplete specimen that must have been more than 20 mm wide.

Brachial interior: The triangular, concave hinge plates are discrete and inclined toward the midline. At the medial edge, each is joined to a small vertical plate that projects above the surface of the hinge plates. This pair of plates diverging from the beak with a narrow, groovelike cavity between them corresponds to the bilobed "cardinal process" of Boucot (1957a, p. 318). The hinge plates are supported posteriorly by secondary shell material and laterally by the thickened socket walls. The inner edges of the hinge plates are extended to form broad crural bases; spires not preserved. Anterior to the cardinalia, a narrow, low, median myophragm splits the deep trough formed by the brachial fold and reaches midlength. Muscle scars not discernible.

Pedicle interior: Prominent, medially convex dental plates support the teeth and border the narrow delthyrial cavity. The dental plates extend beneath the interarea from the beak along the delthyrium margin to the teeth, but are joined to the floor only in their posterior part. They converge toward the median septum near the beak, but a small, secondary deposit obscures them. These plates can not be seen to join the septum. The thin, median septum begins at the apex of the delthyrial cavity and increases in elevation to about midlength where it ends abruptly. Extensive secondary thickening in the umbonal and delthyrial cavities is lacking.

DISCUSSION: Eight specimens were found from three localities, only one poorly preserved shell shows the pedicle interior, three the brachial interior.

These specimens differ from other species of *K.* (*Megakozlowskiella*) only in having the brachial valve moderately convex rather than strongly so. The cardinalia are nearly identical to those in specimens illustrated by Boucot (1957a, Pl. 3, fig. 17) from the Birdsong Shale and by Amsden (1958, Pl. 8, fig. 13—*K.* (*M*) *velata*) from the Haragan Formation.

Swartz (1929, p. 56, Pl. 7, figs. 18–20) recognized this form as a variety of *K.* (*M*) *perlamellosus* (Hall, 1857) principally because of its smaller size, but it is here separated as a distinct species because of its less convex brachial valve, flatter pedicle interarea and less incurved beak.

K. (*M.*) *cyrtinoides* (Dunbar, 1920, p. 138, Pl. 4, figs. 1–3) from western Tennessee differs in the structure of its pedicle interior. In it, the dental plates unite with the median septum before reaching the shell bottom.

K. (*M.*) *octocostata tennesseensis* (Dunbar, 1920, p. 139, Pl. 4, figs. 8–9) is more transverse, more strongly biconvex, and the beak is more incurved than this species.

K. (*M.*) *octocostata* (Hall, 1857, p. 62) is probably a Keyser Limestone species: the type locality was cited as "limestones of the Lower Helderberg group," at Cumberland, Maryland. Compared with *K.* (*M.*) *octocostata*, *K.* (*M.*) *praenuntia* has a broader and more prominent brachial fold, and a shorter brachial interarea. The valves of *K.* (*M.*) *octocostata* are subequally convex, whereas the brachial valve is much less convex than the pedicle in *K.* (*M.*) *praenuntia.*

K. (M.) velata Amsden (1958, p. 121, Pl. 8, figs. 1–13, Pl. 12–F, and Fig. 13) from the Haragan Formation of Oklahoma may be distinguished from this species by its more widely spaced, frilly lamellae and fewer lateral plications.

K. (M.) missouriensis (Tansey, 1922, p. 199, Pl. 51, figs. 1–11) from the Bailey Limestone of Missouri is a nearly identical species, but it apparently has extensive secondary deposits in the pedicle umbonal cavities similar to *K. (M.) velata.* Since such deposits are yet unknown in Keyser specimens, the two species are retained pending further study.

OCCURRENCE: 16:135–156, 24:218–230, 240–266.

Subfamily DELTHYRINAE Waagen, 1883
Genus *Howellella* Kozlowski, 1946 (= *Crispella* Kozlowski, 1929)
Type species: *Delthyris elegans* Muir-Wood, 1925

Howellella modesta (Hall, 1857)
(Pl. 6, figs. 21–28)

Spirifer modesta HALL, 1857, p. 61
Spirifer modestus HALL, 1859, p. 203, Pl. 28, figs. 1a–f; MAYNARD, 1913, p. 399–400, Pl. 68, figs. 17–22; SWARTZ, 1929, p. 56, Pl. 6, figs. 16–17; SWARTZ, 1939, p. 383, Pl. 1, figs. 7a–b
Spirifer modestus var. *plicatus* MAYNARD, 1913, Pl. 68, figs. 23–24; SWARTZ, 1929, Pl. 6, figs. 18–19; SWARTZ, 1939, Pl. 1, figs. 8a–c

DESCRIPTION: Shell wider than long, pedicle valve deeper than brachial; cardinal margins smoothly rounded with the greatest width anterior to the hinge line. Anterior margin rounded, straight or slightly extended in a round tongue. Pedicle interarea small, curved, apsacline, less than half shell width. Brachial interarea anacline, narrow, extending slightly more than half shell width. Pedicle beak prominent, pointed, erect to incurved; the cardinal slopes concave. Delthyrium higher than wide with small deltidial plates perpendicular to the interarea, coalescing at the apex to form a small, convex plate. Brachial beak small, not incurved. The pedicle median sulcus begins near the beak and is round to subangular in cross-section. It varies from indistinct to well defined but is always present. The lateral slopes of both valves smooth or plicate, the plications varying from barely discernible to distinct, but they are never more than low, rounded crenulations in the surface. The bracial medial fold in some specimens distinct only at the anterior where is it emphasized by the uniplicate commissure. It is rounded in cross-section and only rarely shows any traces of a slight depression along its crest. The surface is also ornamented by weak, irregularly spaced growth lines and minute, radial ridges (=spine bases).

Brachial interior: Cardinalia similar to *Delthyris;* large, diverging dental sockets supported by short crural plates which are convex toward the midline. The crural plates do not meet along the midline as in *Delthyris hyndmanensis;* instead, they diverge at 25 to 30 degrees. The area of diductor attachment is variably marked by longitudinal grooves separated by thin, parallel plates. On some specimens a shallow groove parallel to the dental socket is present on each crural plate. A low myophragm extends from near the beak to midlength. A pair of lateral, rounded elevations which are internal reflections of the external fold boundaries diverge from the beak at about 20 degrees.

Pedicle interior: Dental plates well developed, support small, blunt teeth. They diverge at about 30 degrees anteriorly, extend to one-fourth to one-half valve length and define umbonal cavities. A median myophragm is usually present as a flat or grooved elevation which extends from the anterior edge of the delthyrial cavity to midlength or beyond. Longitudinally striated muscle impressions are present between the myophragm and the dental plates anterior to the delthyrial cavity in well preserved shells. The anterior boundary of the muscle field is obscure, but the posterior is marked by a pair of rounded depressions.

Measurements: Plicated specimens indicated by *.

Length	Width	Length	Width	Length	Width
15 mm	17 mm	11	11	*11	12.5
*15	18	*11	12.5	13	14
*12	14	12	14	*11	12
15	19	15	16	13	14
*14	16	16	17	12	13
13	15	*14	17	*12	13
*14	15	14	14	10	11
14	17	*15	16	12	14
*12	14	14	15	13	15
12	15	*12	14	14	16
12	14	13.5	14	*16	18

DISCUSSION: *Howellella modesta* can be distinguished from most other *Howellella* species by its lack of prominent plications.

In Hall's original description of *H. modesta* (1857, p. 61) from the limestones of the Lower Helderberg Group (Keyser Limestone) Cumberland, Maryland, no mention was made of lateral plications. When plicate forms were found later, they were given a separate "varietal" name (*H. modesta* var. *plicatus*) by Maynard (1913, p. 400). Since there is a gradation from smooth to plicate shells in the writer's collection, only one name is necessary.

H. modesta is quite similar to *H. corallinensis* (Grabau, 1900, p. 352) from the Cobleskill of New York. Berdan (1949, p. 217) examined the types of the two species and noted that *H. modesta* has a more feeble fold and sulcus, shows less evidence of plications, is less transverse and has a more erect pedicle beak. These features are variable in both species, however, and it is questionable whether a significant difference exists between them.

H. pauciplicata Waite (1956, p. 15–18, Pl. 3) from the Upper Silurian of the Great Basin is like *H. modesta* externally, but it is uncertain from Waite's figures whether they are identical in interior structure.

OCCURRENCE: 5:116–120, 7:36–44, 8:0–12, 12:65–90, 108–133, 13:65–134, 16:73–144, 21:96–140, 22:0–93, 24:10–45, 25:59–99.

Howellella vanuxemi (Hall, 1859)
(Pl. 6, figs. 29–33)

Spirifer vanuxemi HALL, 1859, p. 198, Pl. 8, figs. 21–23; MAYNARD, 1913, p. 403, Pl. 68, figs. 32–33

DESCRIPTION: Transversely oval, width always greater than length. Cardinal margins smoothly rounded so that the greatest width is near or just posterior to the middle. Biconvex in profile with the pedicle valve the deeper of the two. Pedicle interarea small but high, curved, apsacline; beak small, suberect, erect to weakly incurved. Brachial interarea short, flat, more distinct than pedicle, anacline to nearly orthocline; beak small, barely elevated above hinge line, erect to faintly incurved. Delthyrium higher than wide, modified by narrow, flangelike deltidial plates normal to the interarea. At the apex, they join to form a small convex plate. A broad median fold is present on the brachial valve. The fold is often a little flattened and may be slightly depressed along the middle. Three or four rounded plications are common on each side of the fold with the marginal ones being indistinct; rarely five plications are found. On the pedicle valve, the shallow sulcus is bordered by four or five plications. The prominence of the plications varies considerably between individuals, being quite marked on some and barely discernible on others. Closely spaced, nonfrilly growth lines are present over the entire surface, and minute radial ridges (=spine bases) are rarely preserved.

Brachial interior: Cardinalia similar to *H. modesta* but differ in several striking respects. The dental sockets are long, narrow slits which expand gradually away from the beak. The outer socket wall is attached to the undersurface of the brachial interarea which projects over its edge. The inner socket wall is supported by diverging crural plates inclined toward the midline. The plates do not meet and are joined to the floor only at the posterior. They do not extend anteriorly as ridges; however, about half-way between the sockets and the valve floor, the plates project anteriorly as thin, narrow ribbons some nearly one-third the valve length. The dorsal or under edge of these plates is nearly straight, radiating from the point where the crural plates join the valve floor. In the apex of the notothyrium a small, variable, striated deposit served as the seat of attachment for the diductors. It is commonly bilobed but may be multilobed or consist of tiny, thin, longitudinal plates.

Pedicle interior: The small, blunt teeth are supported by receding dental lamellae diverging from the beak and sloping laterally. The plates are nearly flat and join the floor of the valve not far from the posterior; they do not extend anteriorly as ridges. Diductor scars not impressed. The crest of the central fold, the internal reflection of the pedicle sulcus, may be accentuated or be flattened in a narrow, elongate adductor track, but a distinct myophragm is missing.

DISCUSSION: This species is closely related to *H. modesta,* and externally some specimens of these two species resemble each other, but they can be separated easily on the internal structure of either valve.

Howellella vanuxemi was originally described from the Manlius of New York but has also been reported from the Manlius of New Jersey (Weller, 1903, p. 262, Pl. 24, figs. 9–12), the Tonoloway and Wills Creek Formations of Maryland (Prouty and Swartz, 1923, p. 447, Pl. 23, figs. 5–9) and the Keyser.

Schuchert (1913, p. 403) established a new "variety," *H. vanuxemi* var. *prognosticus,* for the Maryland Keyser specimens bearing five to six plications on each side of the fold. The writer found no specimens with six plications, and most of the shells have only four.

H. vanuxemi minor (Weller, 1903, p. 238, Pl. 21, figs. 41–42) from the Decker Formation of New Jersey differs but little from *H. vanuxemi vanuxemi* from which it was originally distinguished by being smaller and in having less conspicuous concentric markings.

H. vanuxemi hartnageli Howell (1947, p. 2, Pl. 2, figs. 1–4) from the Cobleskill Formation of New York was separated by being proportionally wider and having a better developed groove on the brachial fold.

H. cycloptera (Hall, 1857, p. 58) from the New York Helderberg Group has five to seven rounded plications on each flank and is larger than *H. vanuxemi.* Specimens of this species from the Bois d'Arc Formation in Oklahoma have double-barreled spines (Amsden, 1963; p. 110).

H. crispus from the Niagara Group (Hall, 1852, p. 262, Pl. 54, figs. 3a–k) has a long, wide, flat, well developed interarea, and five or six, rarely eight, plications on each flank.

H. exiquus (Foerste, 1909, p. 17, Pl. 1, figs. 8a–c) is more rounded laterally, and the lateral plications are less distinct than in *H. vanuxemi.*

H. ohioensis (Grabau, 1910, p. 134, Pl. 18, figs. 1–3, Pl. 29, figs. 4–5) was originally distinguished from *H. vanuxemi* by being about twice as large, and the plications are fewer, wider apart and diminish rapidly away from the midline.

H. keyserensis (Swartz, 1923, p. 449, Pl. 23, figs. 13–14) from the Tonoloway Limestone of West Virginia hardly differs from *H. vanuxemi:* the original distinction was that *H. keyserensis* was much larger (width 17 mm).

H. mckenzicus (Prouty, 1923, p. 446, Pl. 22, figs. 21–30) from the McKenzie Formation has the hinge line more extended and has more numerous (four to ten) and stronger lateral plications than *H. vanuxemi.*

H. smithi Waite (1956, p. 17, Pl. 4, figs. 16–10) from the Upper Silurian of the Great Basin may be distinguished by its longer, wider and better developed pedicle interarea.

H. lirata Talent (1956, Pl. 10, figs. 4–7) from the Devonian Buchan Caves Limestone of Australia has five or six strong, subangular plications on each lateral slope.

As can be inferred from the above comparisons, the Silurian species of *Howellella* related to *H. vanuxemi* are much in need of restudy. New species have been defined on very minor features and often the authors were unable to obtain a clear idea of the distinguishing characters of the other species. A restudy of large collections (not just types) of these spiriferids will undoubtedly place many of the old species in synonymy.

OCCURRENCE: 9:6.5–10, 12:230–259, 13:15–65, 14:17–23.5, 16:185–198, 24:10–45, 126–147, 197–211.

Genus *Delthyris* Dalman, 1828
Type species: *Delthyris elevata* Dalman, 1828

Delthyris hyndmanensis n. sp.
(Pl. 6, figs. 34–43)

DESCRIPTION: Outline transverse, cardinal and anterolateral margins smoothly rounded; greatest width at or a little anterior to the hinge line. Strongly biconvex, pedicle valve the deeper. Pedicle beak incurved, pointed; interarea apsacline, high and curved; the width a little less than hinge line width. Beak ridges rounded and indistinct. Delthyrium higher than wide; deltidial plates small and bladelike, attached to the sides of the delthyrium normal to the interarea and projecting posteriorly. The plates were not observed to reach the apex of the delthyrium. Brachial beak small, suberect to incurved, barely extending above the hinge line; interarea short, anacline to orthocline, approximately half shell width. A rounded, median fold extends from the beak to the anterior; it is rarely slightly flattened along the crest and no median groove is present. Two distinct, more or less angular plications are present on each side of the fold, and some large specimens have an indistinct third lateral plication, but only rarely is this well developed. The pedicle sulcus is rounded in cross-section and is bounded by three plications; on a few larger specimens a small fourth lateral plication is present. The commissure is strongly serrate. Surface ornamented by well developed but nonfrilly growth lamellae which bear a fringe of minute radial spines.

Brachial interior: Short crural plates are supported laterally by the convex inner wall of the large dental sockets. At the posterior, the plates converge toward the midline at the bottom of the valve to form a U-shaped depression with the crural plates cemented to the floor. They do not extend anteriorly as ridges. A low, median myophragm extends for one-third shell length. A feeble pair of elongate-oval adductor scars are impressed near midlength. The area of diductor attachment between the crural plates is longitudinally striated.

Pedicle interior: Teeth supported by strong dental plates diverging from the beak at 30 to 40 degrees; the plates extend for about one-quarter valve length, but continue as ridges to near midlength. Just below the edge of the delthyrium, the plates slope toward the midline, but are then deflected perpendicular to the bottom of the valve. A well developed, thin, median septum extends from the beak, increasing gradually in elevation to near midlength before descending abruptly. The septum is swollen beneath the beak in some specimens.

DISCUSSION: This species has probably been mistaken by earlier workers for *Kozlowskiellina octocostata* (Hall, 1857, p. 62). That species may also be from the Keyser Limestone, but it is uncertain because Hall identified the type locality as "Limestones of the Lower Helderberg group, Cumberland (Md.)." The writer found no specimens of this species in the Keyser. Compared to *Delthyris hyndmanensis*, *K. octocostata* has more prominent, frilly growth lamellae, and it has more plications, four on each lateral slope instead two or three.

D. hyndmanensis differs from other species of *Delthyris* in normally having only two plications on each lateral slope of the brachial valve, and three on each lateral slope of the pedicle valve.

D. kozlowskii Amsden (1951) from the Henryhouse Formation of Oklahoma is similar to the Keyser specimens, but can be distinguished by having four or five plications on the lateral slopes of each valve, and more strongly developed growth lamellae.

D. saffordi (Hall, 1859, p. 203, Pl. 28, fig. 2) from the New Scotland Limestone of New York has four to six plications on each lateral slope, and is smaller in size than *D. hyndmanensis*.

D. trescotti Williams (1917, p. 77, Pl. 1, figs. 1–9, 11, 20, 22–23, 25) from the Edmunds Formation of Maine has four plications on each lateral slope, and the fold and sulcus are wider and flatter than in *D. hyndmanensis*.

D. rugaecosta (Hall) from the Stonehouse Formation from Arisaig, Nova Scotia, bears six or seven lateral plications on each valve and a groove in the brachial sulcus; on some specimens there is a small plication in the pedicle groove (McLearn, 1924, p. 82–83). *D. rugaecosta* mut. *prima* McLearn (1924) is like the normal *D. rugaecosta* except that it is smaller and has three or four lateral plications on the dorsal valve. *D. rugaecosta* var. *subsulcata* (Hall) lacks the groove in the brachial fold but has five or six lateral plications on the brachial valve (McLearn, 1924, p. 84).

D. pegramensis (Foerste 1903, p. 710) from the Brownsport of Tennessee has no lateral plications.

Spirifer (Quadrifarius) loculatus Fuchs (1923) and *Quadrifarius loculatus* var. *crassifissa* Fuchs (1929) are both larger and more alate than the species from the Keyser. They have six or more lateral plications which are more rounded, and the brachial fold has a slight groove.

Spirifer (Delthyris) magnus Kozlowski (1929) from Poland is much larger and is alate; it has six or more lateral plications on each valve, and a small fold in the pedicle sulcus and a groove in the brachial fold.

D. dumontianus (de Koninck; illustrated by Boucot, 1957, Pl. 1, fig. 1–6) from the European Gedinnian has six or more plications on each lateral slope.

D. elevata Dalman (1828, as originally figured) has a much higher area, less incurved beak and five lateral plications on the pedicle valve. *D. elevata* as figured and described by Kozlowski (1929) from Podolia resembles the Keyser species, but it has three to six lateral plications on the brachial valve, four to seven on the pedicle valve.

The resemblance between the Keyser species, *D. hyndmanensis,* and *D. kozlowskii, D. saffordi, D. trescotti,* and *D. elevata* is strong; but because they consistently have fewer plications, they are here made a separate species. The name is derived from the type locality of the species, Hyndman, Pennsylvania, Locality 5.

HOLOTYPE: MCZ 9486b. Pl. 6, figs. 35–37.

PARATYPES: MCZ 9486a,c.

TYPE LOCALITY: Hyndman, Pennsylvania, Locality 5, Keyser Limestone, 116 to 120 feet above the base of the formation.

OCCURRENCE: 5:116–120, 6:16–33, 11:30–37, 12:15–65, 65–133, 13:15–90, 25:70–99.

Superfamily STRINGOCEPHALACEA King, 1850
Family CENTRONELLIDAE Waagen, 1882
Subfamily RENSSELAERIINAE Raymond, 1923
Genus *Nanothyris* Cloud, 1942
Type species: *Meganteris mutabilis* Hall, 1857

Nanothyris mutabilis (Hall, 1857)
(Pl. 7, figs. 4–10)

Meganteris mutabilis HALL, 1857, p. 97

Rensselaeria mutabilis HALL, 1859, p. 254, Pl. 45, figs. 2a–2p; SCHUCHERT, 1913, p. 378–379, Pl. 66, figs. 5–6

Rensselaeria (Beachia) proavita SCHUCHERT, 1913, p. 385, Pl. 67, figs. 1–3

DESCRIPTION: Shell of moderately small size, subpentagonal to elongate-oval in outline. Biconvex in lateral profile, the pedicle valve deeper than the brachial. In transverse profile, the brachial valve is evenly convex, but the pedicle valve is strongly convex over the middle and flatter on the sides. Varying from subdued to well-developed, 26 to 30 costellae ornament the margins of the valves. The posterior one-half to two-thirds is smooth in many specimens, but in some the costellae extend to the posterior half of the shell. Growth lines vary from inconspicuous to pronounced. Brachial beak small and inconspicuous. Pedicle beak pointed, suberect to erect, elevated over the brachial beak. Delthyrium modified by small deltidial plates which were not observed to coalesce in the middle, but this may be due to incomplete preservation. Beak ridges rounded, bordering small, curved palintropes. Anterior margin rectimarginate and crenulate. Shell punctate.

Brachial interior: Broad, triangular hinge plates are slightly concave and are joined across the middle by a single convex plate which is perforate at the apex. Crural plates are developed to varying degrees; in some specimens extending only a short distance as plates, but continuing anteriorly as ridges; and, in others, they are well developed, strong supports thickened by secondary deposition of shell material. The dental sockets are long slits which expand laterally; the lateral edges of the hinge plates project over the sockets to make a firm articulation. A feeble, median myophragm may be present in the central part of the valve separating the indistinctly impressed longitudinally elongate adductor scars; central and lateral adductor scar pairs cannot be distinguished. Crura formed by continuation of the inner edges of the hinge plates. Crural points broad; loop centronelliform with a rather large transverse plate.

Pedicle interior: Teeth small, slightly incurved and supported by distinct, thin dental plates which extend only a short distance anteriorly. The dental plates and umbonal cavities have not been covered with secondary shell material. Muscle scars not seen.

DISCUSSION: Schuchert (1913, p. 385) recognized two closely related terebratuloid species in the Keyser of Maryland, *N. mutabilis* (Hall, 1857) and *N. proavita*, which he named the smooth, subpentagonal specimens. Both forms are found in the Keyser, but since small specimens of the two are alike, and large specimens occur together in the same rocks, as at Selinsgrove, Pennsylvania, and apparently intergrade completely, the two are considered synonymous.

OCCURRENCE: 1:128–138, 12:170–212, 24:197–211, 214–228, 26:14–15, 31–33.

Nanothyris boucoti n. sp.
(Pl. 7, figs. 1–3)

DESCRIPTION: Subcircular to transversely oval in outline, greatest width near midlength. Strongly biconvex in lateral profile with the pedicle valve deeper than the brachial. In anterior profile, the greatest curvature is over the midportion of the pedicle valve while the lateral slopes are more flattened; brachial valve more evenly convex. In the largest specimen, the anterior and lateral margins are abrupt, nearly perpendicular to the plane of contact. Pedicle umbo inflated, beak erect or a little incurved, elevated over brachial beak. Small, but distinct, beak ridges border a small, curved palintrope. Brachial beak small, not conspicuous. Anterior commissure rectimarginate and crenulate. Very weak costellae are present at the margins, at least 33 on the largest specimen. Delthyrial modifications not seen.

Brachial interior: Cardinal plate concave, perforate at the posterior and supported by discrete crural plates. Loop not preserved in the one specimen sectioned.

Pedicle interior: Teeth supported by thin, short dental plates which extend for a short distance anteriorly as low, rounded ridges. Muscle scars not seen.

Measurements: A fourth specimen was incomplete but approximately the same size as No. 2; this specimen was serially sectioned (Fig. 6).

Length	Width	Thickness
17.0 mm	17.2 mm	12.9 mm
16.5	17.9	11.4
14.7	13.1	10.1

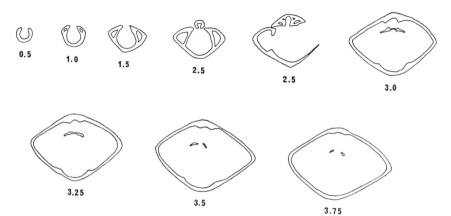

0.5 1.0 1.5 2.5 2.5 3.0 3.25 3.5 3.75

Figure 6. *Serial sections of* Nanothyris boucoti *n. sp.* The distance from the posterior is given in millimeters. Note the short, thin dental plates in the pedicle valve and the very short but distinct crural plates supporting the cardinal plate. The crural plates appear to be composed of two plates that are separate at the bottom but fuse to support the cardinal plate. ($\times$ 2)

DISCUSSION: Only four specimens of this species were found in the Keyser Limestone, all from New Creek, West Virginia, Locality 14. Three are large and nearly identical, but the fourth is smaller and elongate rather than transverse. This species is named after A. J. Boucot in appreciation for his assistance in this project.

This species differs from *N. mutabilis* in being larger, more transvere in outline, in having the anterior and lateral margins nearly perpendicular to the commissure, and in having more abundant, feeble costellae near the commissure.

This species resembles *N. mutabilis* figured by Cloud (1942, Pl. 3, figs. 1–12) but differs in being transverse and having only feeble costellae at the margins.

It differs from *N. keyserensis* (Swartz, 1913, p. 384, Pl. 66, figs. 26–28) in being more abruptly curved at the anterior, and in lacking the median sulcus and flattening of the pedicle valve.

HOLOTYPE: MCZ 9487. Pl. 7, figs. 1–3.

TYPE LOCALITY: New Creek, West Virginia, Locality 14, Keyser Limestone, unit 2.

OCCURRENCE: 14:17–23.5

Superfamily RHYNCHONELLACEA Gray, 1848

Family OLIGORHYNCHIIDAE Cooper, 1956

Genus *Rhynchotreta* Hall, 1879

Type species: *Terebratula cuneata* Dalman, 1828

Rhynchotreta? hancockensis n. sp.

(Pl. 7, figs. 18–24, 27)

DESCRIPTION: Triangular in outline with straight, flat posterolateral margins meeting at 70 to 80 degrees in most specimens, but 60 degrees in small ones and flaring to 90 degrees or more in very large specimens. The valves are subequally biconvex with the pedicle valve slightly more convex. The anterior margin is weakly curved. Pedicle beak pointed, nearly straight in small, but increasing to suberect in large specimens. Subapical foramen bounded by small deltidial plates which are discrete, but appear to fuse in larger specimens, although this is not well shown by the specimens at hand. Surface ornamented by 10 to 12 high, angular plications. The central pair of plications on the brachial valve originate a little anterior to, rather than at, the beak, thus producing a faint median depression near the beak. However, toward the front of the shell, the central portion is raised in a gentle fold. On the pedicle valve the three median plications merge near the beak, and only one central plication reaches the posterior. A gentle median sulcus is formed near the front. The anterior commissure is strongly zigzag. Prominent growth lamellae are usually present.

Brachial interior: Broad, triangular hinge plates are supported by plates which join the low median septum to form a wide cruralium. In some cases, the supporting plates appear to originate more from the bottom of the valve than from the septum, but secondary deposits around the septum obscure the bases of the plates. The crura curve to point toward the pedicle valve; they are crescent shaped in cross-section. The hinge plates are supported laterally by the inner socket walls which bound uncrenulated sockets. The median septum reaches midlength. Muscle scars not preserved. No specimen was observed to have the cruralium roofed over by a plate between the hinge plates, but a number of specimens did show small extentions on the inner edges of the hinge plates partially overhanging the cruralium. It seems likely that a complete roofing plate over the anterior part of the cruralium was once present but was not preserved.

Pedicle interior: Small, blunt teeth are supported by thin, short dental plates pressed close to the lateral walls. A shallow groove is present between each tooth and the shell edge where they are joined. Delthyrial cavity moderately deep; muscle scars not preserved.

DISCUSSION: The above description is based on small triangular specimens mostly less than 10 mm in length. Two larger specimens were also found, one 18 mm long, and the other, a broken specimen, of about the same size, which may belong to the same species. Both are pedicle valves showing the same interior structure as the smaller specimens, but they have a pronounced sulcus in the anterior two-thirds of the shell. Each specimen is marked by a prominent growth lamellae at about 7 mm from the beak, and the shape indicated by these growth lines corresponds to that of the small specimens. If the large specimens do belong to the same species, it should be added to the description that a pronounced sulcus develops as the length approaches 10 mm, and additional plications are added anterolaterally, and the sides become more flared.

These specimens are questionably placed in the genus *Rhynchotreta* Hall, 1879, as redefined by St. Joseph (1937, p. 161–176). Hall originally designated *Terebratula cuneata* Dalman, 1828, from Gotland as the type species, but his description of this species was inaccurate. St. Joseph redescribed the type species and pointed out that a cardinal process is not present (contrary to Hall and Clark, 1894, p. 186). Both Hall and St. Joseph mentioned the presence of fine concentric filae on the type species. None were observed on the Keyser specimens, and for this reason the assignment is queried; but since they are all silicified, the absence of filae may be due to imperfect preservation.

R. cuneata (Dalman, 1828) from the Silurian of Europe may be distinguished by its straighter beak, more apical foramen, and greater convexity in the posterior half. Also, the change from a slight median depression at the posterior to a fold at the front in the brachial valve is more marked.

R. cuneata var. *americana* (Hall, 1879, p. 167, Pl. 25, figs. 29–38) reported widely in the Middle Silurian of eastern North America has a more acute posterior angle, and the posterolateral margins flare more abruptly.

The figures of *"Rhynchonella"? bialveata* Hall (1857, p. 73; 1859, p. 233, Pl. 34, figs. 1–4) from the New Scotland Limestone of New York superficially resemble the small Keyser specimens; but they have 12 to 14 plications and are not as broad or distinctly triangular as *R. hancockensis*, and they differ in internal structure.

R. bialveata, described by Weller (1903, p. 327, Pl. 42, figs. 9–10) from the Lower Oriskany of New Jersey can be distinguished by its rib branching pattern: on the pedicle valve the median plication splits near the beak, and another plication is intercalated between them near the middle of the valve; on the brachial valve, the median plication divides near the middle of the valve. The divisions in the Keyser specimens all occur very close to the beak. Also, Weller's specimens show a more acute posterior angle, 55 to 60 degrees, than the Keyser shells.

This may be the same form identified by Schuchert (1913, p. 377, Pl. 66, fig. 4) as *R.? bialveata* from the New Scotland of Maryland for he noted that his specimens were more transverse than Hall's. However, Schuchert's illustration is taken from Hall (1859, Pl. 34, fig. 4) and it is uncertain if they are identical or not.

The small individuals of this species resemble *Tetracamera subcuneata* (Hall) described by Weller (1914, p. 214, Pl. 28, figs. 13–24), but there is a marked difference internally: *Tetracamera* has a spondylium in the pedicle valve with lateral buttress plates between the dental plates and the shell wall which divide the umbonal region into four chambers.

This species is named for its type locality, Hancock Station, West Virginia, Locality 26.

HOLOTYPE: MCZ 9493a. Pl. 7, figs. 19, 22–24.

PARATYPES: MCZ 9492, 9493b, 9494.

TYPE LOCALITY: Hancock Station, West Virginia, Locality 26, Keyser Limestone, unit 1.

OCCURRENCE: 10:4.5–9.5, 24:10–45?, 240–266, 26:31–33.

Family TRIGONIRHYNCHIIDAE Schmidt, 1965
Genus *Cupularostrum* Sartenaer, 1961
Type species: *Cupularostrum recticostatum* Sartenaer, 1961

Cupularostrum litchfieldensis (Schuchert, 1903)
(Pl. 7, figs. 25–26, 28–33)

Rhynchonella? litchfieldensis SCHUCHERT, 1903, p. 167
Rhynchonella agglomerata WELLER, 1903, p. 234–235, Pl. 21, figs. 5–11
Camarotoechia litchfieldensis MAYNARD, 1913, p. 353, Pl. 63, figs. 11–14; SWARTZ, 1929, p. 54, Pl. 6, figs. 3, 5

DESCRIPTION: Outline subtriangular with the posterolateral margins nearly straight, diverging at 80 to 100 degrees. The anterolateral margins are rounded; anterior face vertical. Length greater than width in most, but they may be equal, or the width may be the greater. The maximum width occurs at about midlength or slightly to the anterior. Pedicle beak small, pointed, suberect to erect, arched over the obscure brachial beak. The apex of the beak is pierced by a circular foramen. The delthyrium is bordered by small, narrow deltidial plates. Although they were not observed to be conjunct, the deltidial plates are so poorly preserved that this possibility can not be eliminated. A pedicle sulcus and brachial fold begin about midlength, but they are prominent only at the front where the commissure is strongly uniplicate. The pedicle sulcus continues as a long tongue into the brachial fold, and is nearly perpendicular to the plane of the valves. Surface covered by 15 to 19 simple plications with sharply rounded to angular cross-sections, with three in the sulcus and four on the fold. On many specimens a prominent growth line is present near midlength; smaller zigzag growth lines are present near the margin.

Brachial interior: A covered septalium is present. Each hinge plate is supported medially by a plate which joins the low, stout, median septum. The cover plate is flat to concave at the rear and convex toward the front; no median ridge is present. At the posterior, there is a small perforation joining with the septalial trough in nearly all specimens. The crura are strong, curved toward the pedicle valve; each is crescent shaped in cross-section, concave anteromedially. They originate from the inner edges of the hinge plates which are quite narrow and indistinct. The hinge plates are attached to the inner socket walls and inclined medially. The socket walls are convex medially, and their edges are raised above the hinge plates to produce firm articulation with the other valve. The sockets are uncrenulated. Adductor scars consist of a pair of longitudinal scars on each side of the septum at about midlength. The scars occupy the grooves produced by the plications. Posteriorly and laterally to these is another pair of smaller scars. The inner surface is plicate except for the posterocentral area which is covered by secondary material.

Pedicle interior: Dental plates present, but short, close to the shell walls, defining shallow, umbonal cavities. Teeth small and rounded. Delthyrial cavity large with a broad adductor track extending to nearly one-quarter length. Diductor impression triangular, the posterolateral margins are straight, the anterior margin is undefined but extends to midlength.

Measurements:

Length	Width	Number of plications Pedicle valve	in sulcus
6.5 mm	6.0 mm	17	3
7.5	7.0	19	3
6.5	6.0	17	3
7.5	6.0	16	3
6.5	7.0	19	3
7.5	7.0	19	3
7.0	7.5	17	3
8.0	7.0	19	3
7.5	7.0	17	3
6.5	6.0	17	3
7.5	8.0	19	3
7.0	6.5	19	3
8.0	7.0	15	3
7.0	6.0	17	3
6.0	6.0	15	3
?	6.0	17	3
6.5	5.5	15	3
7.0	7.0	17	3
7.0	7.0	17	3
6.5	6.5	15	3

DISCUSSION: In the past, this species has been assigned to the genus *Camarotoechia* of Hall and Clarke (1894, p. 189) for which *Atrypa congregata* Conrad from the Hamilton Group of New York was designated the type species. The brachial interior was described as containing a septalium not normally roofed over, lacking a cardinal process and typically having crenulated sockets. This diagnosis was followed until recently. Sartenaer (1961a) redescribed topotype specimens of *A. congregata* Conrad, and pointed out that they differ from the so-called "*A. congregata* Conrad" used by Hall and Clarke as the type species of *Camarotoechia*. Sartenaer restricted *Camarotoechia* to forms like *A. congregata* Conrad and assigned the misidentified species of Hall and Clarke to a new genus and species, *Cupularostrum recticostatum*. Many species formerly assigned to *Camarotoechia*, including the present one, belong to this new genus.

Camarotoechia Hall and Clarke, 1894 as now understood includes forms with a rounded outline and a broad posterior angle (120 degrees). The plications are low and rounded with the median ones irregular and increasing by bifurcation and intercalation. A septalium is present in the brachial valve and dental plates in the pedicle valve. Sartenaer (1961b, p. 2) added that the septalium is not covered, but since the specimens are impressions, this probably is still not certain.

Cupularostrum Sartenaer (1961b) includes small to medium size shells with sharply defined fold and sulcus beginning a little in front of the beak. Plications are simple, raised, angular, undivided, and originate at the beak. In the brachial valve the septalium is covered in its anterior part. Although not mentioned by Sartenaer, the sockets of the type specimens do not appear to be crenulated.

This point is important. The type specimens of *Cupularostrum recticostatum* Sartenaer were examined by the writer, and no crenulations were observed in the sockets. In their original description of the genus *Camarotoechia* based on specimens misidentified as *A. congregata* Conrad, Hall and Clarke (1894, p. 190) considered crenulated sockets as a distinctive character of the genus. The specimens they referred to thus differ from both *A. congregata* and *C. recticostatum*. The question arises, what name is to be given specimens that are similar to *C. recticostatum* but which have crenulated sockets? The taxonomic value of socket crenulation in Paleozoic rhynchonelloids is uncertain because it has been observed so rarely, but this feature should be given careful attention in the reassignment of the many so called *Camarotoechia's* of the Paleozoic.

The distinction between *Cupularostrum* and *Ancillotoechia* Havlíček, 1959, is unclear. *Ancillotoechia* also has a covered septalium, but the species assigned to this genus are quite different from *C. litchfieldensis*. The type species (*A. ancillans* Barrande, 1879) differs from the Keyser species in that it has fewer plications, the fold and sulcus are less distinct, the anterior margin is more rounded, and the pedicle beak is not arched over the brachial beak. In the other two species assigned to the genus by Havlíček (1961), *A. minerva* (Barrande) and *A. radvani* Havlíček, 1961, plications are more abundant, but these species are markedly different externally from *C. litchfieldensis*, especially in the appearance of the fold and the plications.

Cupularostrum litchfieldensis is abundant in the lower part of the Keyser Limestone at most localities. The Keyser specimens differ from those from the Decker Formation of New Jersey (Weller, 1903, p. 234) and the Cobleskill Formation of New York (Berdan, 1949, p. 190) in being more variable in the ratio of width to length; the Decker and Cobleskill specimens are wider than long, whereas the Keyser specimens vary from wider than long to longer than wide.

"*Rhynchonella*" *transversa* Hall (1859, p. 234, Pl. 34, figs. 9–16) from the New Scotland Limestone of New York is a similar species, but it has fewer plications than *C. litchfieldensis*.

Camarotoechia? sp. (Amsden, 1958, p. 108–110, Pl. 7, figs. 5–8, Pl. 14, figs. 24–25) from the Haragan Formation probably belongs to *Cupularostrum*. It is similar to the Keyser species, but there are only a few specimens known; these are wider than long and the fold and sulcus begin nearer the umbo than in *Cupularostrum litchfieldensis*.

Although both *C. litchfieldensis* and *C. gordoni* are placed in the genus *Cupularostrum*, it should be noted that the crura of these two species differ and may indicate a less close relationship. In *C. litchfieldensis* the crura are thin, crescent-shaped plates throughout; whereas in *C. gordoni*, the proximal portions are stout and more rodlike. This character cannot be properly evaluated until more is known about its variation in Paleozoic rhynchonelloids.

OCCURRENCE: 5:30–48.5, 116–120, 6:16–33, 75–101, 8:11–17, 11:0–5, 12:0–90, 13:0–134, 16:73–114, 22:0–93, 24:10–66, 102–109, 218–230, 25:70–99.

Cupularostrum gordoni (Maynard, 1913)
(Pl. 7, figs. 34–45; Pl. 8, figs. 1–2)

Uncinulus gordoni MAYNARD, 1913, p. 368, Pl. 65, figs. 1–6
?*Uncinulus keyserensis* SCHUCHERT, 1913, p. 368, Pl. 65, figs. 7–8

DESCRIPTION: Outline suboval to subtriangular; profile strongly biconvex but flattened dorsoventrally, never spherical. The anterior slope commonly abrupt and the brachial valve is deeper than the pedicle valve. In large specimens either the width or length may be the greater, and the thickness is always more than one-half the width. The postero-lateral margins are flat or weakly concave; in dorsoventral view these margins are straight, meeting at an angle of 90 to 110 degrees. The anterolateral margins are evenly rounded. Pedicle beak erect to incurved, pressed closely onto brachial beak so as to obscure the delthyrium. Pedicle accommodated by open delthyrium and small foramen which im-pinges on the pedicle beak. Brachial beak suberect to erect, curved under pedicle beak filling the delthyrium. Surface marked by 12 to 18 subangular to rounded, simple plications which decrease in size toward the umbo and toward the lateral margins; only rarely are median grooves preserved on the plications near the margin. Posterolateral commissure smooth, but the remainder is serrate. A pedicle sulcus and brachial fold begin feebly at 8 or 9 mm from the beak, usually not becoming pronounced features on the surface of the valves; however, they are accentuated by the uniplicate commissure with the pedicle sulcus being extended as a tongue into the brachial fold.

Brachial interior: The cruralium is supported by a low, but stout, median septum, and is roofed over in its anterior part by a small convex plate joined to the hinge plates. In more than 200 silicified specimens showing the brachial cardinalia which were examined, less than 10 percent retain the roofing plate. The posterior portion of the cruralium is open. No cardinal process is present. The hinge plates are convex at their anterior ends but concave at the posterior around the cruralium hole. The sockets are narrow, un-crenulated slits between the lateral walls of the hinge plates and the shell margin: they open in a nearly posterior direction. The median septum generally does not extend to midlength; it separates the feebly to strongly impressed, elongate adductor scars. In some cases the scars can be divided into a posterolateral pair and an anteromedian pair, but in others they form two simple parabolic impressions. The scars are usually set in the grooves produced by the corrugation of the shell and begin a little in front of the cruralium and extend to less than midlength. Secondary shell deposition occurs around the posterior end of the median septum and may thicken the crural bases and crouralial parts, but does not fill in the cruralium. The crura are long, thin and curved so as to point toward the pedicle valve, and are crescent shaped in cross-section at their distal ends, but solid rods or plates where they originate from the hinge plates.

Pallial markings, well preserved on one internal mold, consist of at least six main trunks on each side, one apparently unbranched anteromedian trunk, an anterolateral trunk which bifurcates at least once, and four lateral trunks which branch at least twice before reaching the margin.

Pedicle interior: No plates were seen modifying the delthyrium. Teeth small and blunt, curved posteromedially and joined to the inner surface of the valve. Dental plates short and pressed close to the shell walls, bordering the deep delthyrial cavity. The musculature of this form is unclear to the writer. In all specimens examined there is a deep, elongate and narrow, somewhat triangular scar extending for one-third the valve length. Surrounding this scar is a broad, subcircular field on each side which is rarely discernible as anything more than a slightly rougher region of the shell interior. The pallial trunks radiate from this region. The writer is uncertain if the deep elongate scar represents the adductor seat, and the broad surrounding fields the diductors, or if they represent the diductor and genital areas, respectively. In the first case, both the adductors and diductors would be quite large relative to the shell size: in the second case, the adductor scars are so lightly impressed that they have not yet been detected. A low median myophragm and feeble smaller myophragms are common in the deep elongate scar. Secondary deposition tends to obscure the dental plates and emphasize the muscle scars.

Growth: The shape of this species changes perceptibly during its growth. Young (less than 7 to 8 mm in length) individuals are longer than wide, and the thickness is often less than half the width. No sign of a fold or sulcus appears at this stage. The postero-lateral margins are nearly straight and diverge from the beak at 90 degrees or less, making the outline markedly subtriangular even though the anterior is rounded. The first trace of the fold and sulcus appear when the specimens reach 7 to 9 mm in length. Also, at about this point, the component of growth perpendicular to the plane of contact becomes greater, leading to a gradual increase in thickness relative to length and width. The width also tends to increase relative to length, so that in larger specimens it is not uncommon for the width to be greater than the length.

The number of plications observed varies from 11 to 17, but this is in part a function of the preservation of the small plications on the posterolateral margins of the specimens; there are about 12 well developed plications on most specimens plus a varying number of smaller ones on the lateral slopes. The plications divide on only a few, small specimens.

Measurements: Specimens from Keyser, West Virginia, Locality 12, 212 to 223 feet above the Tonoloway Limestone follow:

| Length | Width | Thickness | Number of plications | | | Sulcus begins * |
			Pedicle	Fold	Sulcus	
6.2 mm	5.4 mm	2.4 mm	13	—	—	—
7.6	6.8	3.3	13	—	—	—
8.5	7.8	3.3	15	—	—	—
8.7	8.3	4.0	14	—	—	—
9.2	8.2	4.5	15	—	—	—
9.4	8.0	4.1	15	—	—	—
9.5	8.6	4.2	17	—	—	—
10.0	9.5	5.1	14	—	—	—
11.0	10.4	6.1	16	4	3	8
11.3	11.5	5.8	14	4	3	9
11.5	10.6	7.4	13	2	1	8
11.5	10.8	6.9	16	4	3	7
11.5	11.0	6.7	15	4	3	7
11.9	11.5	6.4	15	4	3	8
12.5	13.3	9.8	16	5	4	8
12.6	12.0	8.0	16	4	3	9
12.6	12.3	6.7	14	4	3	8
12.7	12.8	8.5	14	4	3	8
13.5	14.2	9.0	15	5	4	9
13.5	14.3	9.6	17	4	3	7
13.5	13.5	8.0	13	4	3	8
13.9	12.2	7.1	15	4	3	8
14.5	13.5	10.0	13	4	3	8
14.6	12.9	8.2	15	4	3	9
14.8	13.7	11.6	15	4	3	9
15.0	16.0	10.2	15	5	4	8
15.0	16.4	10.4	11	3	2	9
15.2	15.8	8.5	13	4	3	10
15.8	14.4	10.8	12	4	3	10
16.1	15.8	11.5	15	4	3	10

* Measured in mm from the beak.

Specimens from New Creek, West Virginia, Locality 14, follow:

| Length | Width | Thickness | Number of plications | | | Sulcus begins * |
			Pedicle	Fold	Sulcus	
8.9 mm	8.0 mm	6.8 mm	13	4	3	6
12.5	13.1	7.2	14	4	3	7
13.0	11.9	9.4	16	5	4	8
13.4	12.6	9.6	16	4	3	7
13.5	13.9	10.4	12	4	3	7
13.6	13.9	10.7	12	4	3	7
14.2	14.9	12.0	15	4	3	8
16.1	15.4	10.4	16	5	5	10
17.4	19.9	10.9	15	6	5	10
17.4	19.6	12.6	15	5	4	9

* Measured in mm from the beak.

DISCUSSION: This species is assigned to the genus *Cupularostrum* because of its non-cuboidal form, simple angular plications, fold and sulcus beginning in front of the beaks, short dental lamellae, and partially covered cruralium.

Maynard (1913) assigned this species to *Uncinulus* Bayle, 1878, apparently on the basis of the external appearance, but because *Uncinulus* is characterized by an undivided hinge plate surmounted by a notched cardinal process (Hall and Clarke, 1894, p. 198; Muir–Wood, 1925, p. 93), the Keyser species must be removed from that genus. It is interesting to note that Berdan (1949, p. 204–205) described the early growth stages of *Uncinulus mutabilis* from the Manlius Limestone of New York as having the crural cavity covered by fused cardinal plates, but with no cardinal process present, but the later growth stages as displaying more inflated shells, a well developed cardinal process and a filled crural cavity. Further study of the early stages of this species may be useful in determining the relationship of *Uncinulus* to other rhynchonelloids.

Except for the spheroidal shape, *Sphaerirhynchia* Cooper and Muir-Wood, 1951 (= *Wilsonella* Nikiforova, 1937 = *Wilsonia* Kayser, 1871) is very similar to *Cupularostrum*. However, it is unclear whether the septalium is covered or not in *Sphaerirhynchia*; to the writer's knowledge this structure has never been adequately illustrated or described in the type species. The original description of the type species, *Terebratula wilsoni* Sowerby (1816, p. 38), from the Silurian of Britain is nondiagnostic and does not mention interior structure. In 1852, Davidson (Pl. 13, fig. 14) illustrated an internal cast which clearly shows the pedicle musculature and brachial septum but not the cruralium. In 1867, he presented the same figure plus others showing the exterior (p. 167, Pl. 23, figs. 1–9), and in describing Sowerby's species, he stated that the hinge plate is divided. Hall and Clarke (1894, p. 197) also described the hinge plate as medially divided (thus, no cover), but they were probably relying either on internal casts of *S. saffordi* (Hall) from Tennessee (earlier considered conspecific with *S. wilsoni* by de Verneuil) or on Davidson's work, or both.

Other authors have assigned species with a covered cruralium to *Sphaerirhynchia*. Kozlowski (1929, p. 159, Pl. 7, figs. 27–34) described *Camarotoechia (Wilsonia) wilsoni* from Poland which he thought was the same as the type species; in the brachial valve of these specimens, the cruralium is in some cases closed by the union of the inner edges of the hinge plates. He also noted that in *C. (Wilsonia) tarda* the cruralium is sometimes roofed over. Amsden (1958, p. 94–99) also assigned two species, *S. glomerosa* and *S. lindenensis*, from the Haragan Formation of Oklahoma to *Sphaerirhynchia;* each has the cruralium covered at the anterior. *Cupularostrum gordoni* differs specifically from each of these four forms, and it probably is not congeneric with any of them.

As pointed out above, the delicate cover over the anterior part of the cruralium is preserved in only a small percentage of the silicified Keyser specimens, and in the internal casts in the writer's collection, the cruralium cover is not detectable. Diagnoses based on internal casts, therefore, should be questioned until serial sections or other preparations clearly demonstrate the structure. The possibillity that the cruralium is covered should not yet be dismissed for *Sphaerirhynchia*.

C. gordoni contrasts strongly with *S. wilsoni* (as illustrated by Davidson, 1867) which is a spheroidal species with the thickness sometimes exceeding the width. The fold and sulcus are barely raised above the flanks and are prominent only because of the strongly uniplicate commissure. There are 30 to 40 rounded plications, 6 to 9 on the fold and sulcus; and near the margin the plications have a small median groove along their crests. No foramen is present. In the nonsilicified specimens of *C. gordoni* a foramen is not always apparent, but in silicified specimens the beak is so consistently perforate that there is little doubt that a foramen is present.

Camarotoechia (Wilsonia) tarda (Barrande), the type species of *Lanceomyonia* Havlicek, is in many respects similar to *C. gordoni*. Both have the same variation in shape, a perforate beak, an anteriorly roofed-over cruralium, and slight dental lamellae. However, *C. gordoni* does not belong to *Lanceomyonia* because the plications extend to the beak in the Keyser shells, whereas the posterior portion of the shell is smooth in species of *Lanceomyonia*.

The outline of *Sphaerirhynchia lindenensis* (Dunbar), described by Amsden (1958, p.

97, Pl. 6, figs. 23–28, Pl. 11, figs. 15–16, Pl. 13, figs. 21–23) from the Haragan Formation of Oklahoma and the Linden Group of Tennessee, is similar to the Keyser species, but they are quite unlike in pedicle musculature: in *S. lindenensis* the adductor area is heart shaped with a dividing ridge and completely surrounded by broad diductor scars. These two species are not congeneric.

These specimens differ from Maynard's description of *C. gordoni* only in having fewer plications (12 to 18 versus 19 to 26). The writer has seen no specimens with more than 20 plications, and the typical number appears to be about 17.

Uncinulus keyserensis Schuchert (1913, p. 368, Pl. 65, figs. 7–8) is probably just a somewhat globular specimen of *C. gordoni*.

Compared with *C. convexorus* this species is flatter with a well developed fold and sulcus always present. That species is also more pinched in appearance.

C. obtusiplicata (Hall, 1852, p. 279, Pl. 58, figs. 2a–h) from the Niagara Group of New York and from the McKenzie Formation of Maryland (Swartz, 1923, p. 438, Pl. 21, figs. 4–12) is quite similar to the Keyser species. Hypotypes of the McKenzie specimens (USNM 142834–142839) show the same total range of shape as the Keyser specimens, but can be distinguished by having a more prominent fold and typically a more spheroidal shape.

"*Rhynchonella*" *nucleolata* Hall (1857, p. 68; 1859, p. 227, Pl. 31, figs. 1–2) from the New Scotland Formation as originally figured included a considerable variation in form. Schuchert (1913, p. 364) separated Figures 1a–c of Hall as a distinct species, "*R.*" *globulus*, characterized by its spherical form. The remaining figures still represent a wide range of variation and are difficult to distinguish from *C. gordoni*. The main distinctions are that "*R.*" *nucleolata* has a much higher anterior face, greater proportional thickness, and the plications are more numerous (15 to 23).

OCCURRENCE: 10:4.5–9.5, 12:108–121?, 212–230, 13:15–65?, 14:17–23.5, 57–71, 24:211–266, 25:0–41.

Cupularostrum convexorus (Maynard, 1913)
(Pl. 8, figs. 3–7)

Uncinulus convexorus MAYNARD, 1913, p. 368, Pl. 65, figs. 9–14

DESCRIPTION: Outline elongate, somewhat tear shaped; anterior and lateral portions smoothly rounded, but the posterolateral margins are straight, meeting in a sharp angle of 65 to 80 degrees. Strongly biconvex in profile with the brachial valve deeper than the pedicle; the anterior margin is abrupt. The posterolateral margins are weakly concave and combined with the pointed posterior give the shell a pinched appearance. A brachial fold and pedicle sulcus are very weakly developed on a few specimens, but usually they are wanting. The anterior margin is slightly uniplicate. The erect pedicle beak extends above the brachial beak and is not closely curved over it. Structures around the delthyrium not preserved. Surface ornamented by 20 to 25, rarely 30, low, rounded costae. Those near the lateral margins are quite faint. Maynard's observation (p. 369) that thirty or more plications are present on this species is inaccurate for most of the specimens collected by the writer and also for two of his own illustrated specimens (Pl. 65, figs. 9–13) which have only 20 plications, and for the type specimen which has 27.

Brachial interior: Cardinalia as in *C. gordoni;* anterior part of cruralium covered by a convex plate joining the hinge plates. The median septum is higher than in *C. gordoni* and extends to midlength, dividing the small but clearly impressed muscle field near the middle of the valve. The divergent, elongate adductor scars can be divided into a posterolateral pair and an anteromedian pair; their anterior margins are vague.

Pedicle interior: Interior as in *C. gordoni*. The blunt, curved teeth are supported by thin, short dental plates which define small umbonal cavities. The diductor (?) field is located anterior to the delthyrial cavity and extends to midlength. The adductor scars cannot be clearly discerned, but the diductor area is triangular with a median myophragm extending to the vague anterior margin of the field. "Genital" area not observed.

DISCUSSION: This species is less abundant than *C. gordoni* and can be distinguished from it by the characteristic pinched appearance of its posterior, and the subspherical anterior end which is usually devoid of a fold or sulcus.

OCCURRENCE: 5:30–48.5, 116–120, 6:16–33, 11:37–62, 12:40–65, 90–133, 13:103–134, 16:73–114, 21:59–87, 24:102–109.

Family RHYNCHOTREMATIDAE Schuchert, 1913

Genus *Machaeraria* Cooper, 1955
Type species: *Rhynchonella formosa* Hall, 1857

Machaeraria whittingtoni n. sp.
(Pl. 8, figs. 21–29)

DESCRIPTION: Outline transversely oval, width greater than length: lateral margins smoothly rounded, anterior margin rounded or straight. The posterolateral margins are only weakly curved, meeting at an angle of 110 to 130 degrees. Profile strongly biconvex, the brachial valve being the more convex. Pedicle beak not extended far posterior to the brachial beak, suberect to nearly straight, and perforated at the apex by a round, permesothyrid foramen. The apical portion of the delthyrium covered by small, conjunct deltidial plates. The anterior commissure is strongly uniplicate and crenulate. A brachial fold and pedicle sulcus begin just anterior to the umbos and become pronounced at the front. The pedicle sulcus is extended as a tongue into the brachial fold. Three plications are most commonly present on the fold, two in the sulcus. There are 20 to 25 simple, angular plications on each valve. Weak, concentric growth lines are present especially near the margin.

Brachial interior: The concave, triangular hinge plates are discrete; each is joined laterally to the inner socket wall which is convex toward the midline. The crura extend from the inner edges of the hinge plates, curve ventrally and are crescent shaped in cross-section, concave toward the midline. They continue posteriorly along the under-edge of the hinge plates and join the floor of the valve in platelike secondary deposits (in some specimens resembling true crural plates) which continue as subdued ridges for a short distance anteriorly. A thin, platelike cardinal process is present in the notothyrial cavity. A low, median myophragm extends to one-third length. Muscle scars not impressed. The dental sockets are not crenulated. The specimens show no tendency for hinge plates to grow toward each other over the notothyrial cavity.

Pedicle interior: Small, blunt teeth are supported by short dental plates defining shallow umbonal cavities and extending along the inner surface of the valve for a short distance as low ridges. Muscle field moderately impressed anterior to the large delthyrial cavity. The adductor scars are oval, barely separated in the middle, and surrounded by the subflabellate diductor field. A low ridge marks the lateral edges of the field, but the anterior edge is usually obscure. The underside of the deltidial plates is thickened, thereby partially restricting the delthyrial cavity and forming a short "sheath" for the pedicle.

DISCUSSION: This is probably the Keyser Limestone species identified by Maynard (1913, p. 349, Pl. 62, figs. 25–29) as *Stenochisma formosa;* but since he merely quoted the description from Hall (1859) and took the illustrations from Hall (1859, Pl. 35, figs. 6a, c, d, o and p), Maynard's observations are of little value.

The specimen illustrated by Hall (1859, Pl. 35, figs. 60, p, r) from the Becraft of New York was selected by Cooper (1955, p. 56) as the type for the species *R. formosa* Hall, 1857 and the type species of his genus *Machaeraria*. The principal difference between the Keyser species and *M. formosa* is that the latter has disjunct deltidial plates and lacks a permesothrid foramen. It also has, in the brachial valve, inner hinge plates which almost meet in some specimens. In other respects the two are quite similar, and they are here considered congeneric until more is known about the variations in foramen position in other species.

Machaeraria formosa identified by Weller (1903, p. 309, Pl. 36, figs. 12–15) from the New Scotland and Becraft of New Jersey is more subrhomboidal in outline, has the anterior face inclined, and has fewer plications than the Keyser specimens. The pedicle beak was not described, and a foramen is not indicated in Weller's figures. *M. formosa* described by Weller (1903, p. 328, Pl. 42, figs. 5–8) from the Lower Oriskany has an incurved pedicle beak lacking a permesothyrid foramen. It is also more elongate and has a smaller pedicle angle (78 to 110 degrees) than this species. Neither of Weller's forms appears to be conspecific with *M. formosa* (Hall), or with *M. whittingtoni.*

Machaeraria deckerensis (Weller, 1903, p. 234, Pl. 21, figs. 1–4) from the Decker Formation of New Jersey was originally distinguished from *M. formosa* (Hall) by its coarser plications, greater width and lesser thickness. It is assumed to differ from the Keyser species in lacking a permesothyrid foramen. No mention was made of a pedicle foramen by Weller and his plates do not show one: his specimens are not now available for comparison. Maynard (1913, p. 349) assigned some Keyser specimens to Weller's species *M. deckerensis:* he quoted Weller's description and added only that *M. deckerensis* may be a variety of *M. formosa* (Hall). Maynard's figures show no foramen, but the hypotypes (USNM 142840–142841) have a permesothyrid foramen. Maynard's specimens are merely broad specimens of the species at hand.

Tansey (1922, p. 192, Pl. 48, figs. 20–22) identified one specimen from the Bailey Limestone of Missouri as *M. formosa* (Hall), but it is questionable whether his poorly illustrated specimen actually belongs to that species. It has four plications in the sulcus and five on the fold, more than is commonly present in either *M. formosa* (three and four or *M. whittingtoni* (two and three). The description is quoted from Hall (1859). so it must be assumed the beak lacks a permesothyrid foramen; the figures are inconclusive.

This species is named after H.B. Whittington in appreciation for his guidance of the writer's studies in paleontology.

HOLOTYPE: MCZ 9502a. Pl. 8, figs. 21–22, 28.

TYPE LOCALITY: Hyndman, Pennsylvania, Locality 5, Keyser Limestone 116 to 120 feet above the base of the formation.

OCCURRENCE: 1:46–128, 3:20–26, 5:30–48.5, 116–120, 6:16–33, 7:60–70, 10:4.5–9.5, 11–17, 12:15–65, 13:15–65, 15:36–51, 16:15–59, 24:175–185.

Family Uncertain

Genus *Boucotella* Bowen, 1966
Type species: *Camarotoechia gigantea* Maynard, 1913

Boucotella gigantea (Maynard, 1913)
(Pl. 8, figs. 8–20)

Camarotoechia gigantea MAYNARD, 1913, p. 354, Pl. 63, figs. 15–16
Camarotoechia gigantea var. *gigas* SWARTZ, 1929, p. 55, Pl. 6, figs. 29–31

DESCRIPTION: Subtriangular in outline, posterolateral margins nearly straight, extending to about midlength. Anterolateral margins smoothly curved. Subtriangular in lateral profile with the brachial valve the more convex; greatest thickness near the anterior edge. Pedicle valve more convex in the umbonal region. The pedicle beak is incurved closely over the brachial beak. A broad, median sulcus begins at about 8 to 10 mm from the beak, becoming pronounced at the front. Anterior face nearly vertical, anterior profile subtriangular. Sixteen to twenty subangular plications originate at the beak on each valve; five or six occupy the pedicle sulcus. The brachial fold is prominent only near the front. Commisure strongly uniplicate and crenulate.

Brachial interior: Cardinal process large and prominent, consists of a broad, concave, tonguelike structure extending posterior to the beak, and when in place, completely filling the delthyrial cavity. The process originates from two crural plates which rise vertically from the floor of the valve and flare out posteriorly. A deep groove separates the crural plates at the front. Stout, straight crura project ventrally from the vertical plates. The dental sockets are deeply set between the shell wall and the crural plates. A ridge along the outer surface of these plates overhangs the socket making a secure articulation. Muscle scars are not known since only the umbonal part of the brachial interior has been found. A broad, rounded median ridge begins in front of the cardinal process.

Pedicle interior: Large teeth are curved posteromedially and supported by dental plates which are obscured by later shell deposition or free only at their anterior edges. Shell quite thick in the posterior part. Apex of the delthyrium and delthyrial cavity closed by a concave pair of deltidial plates which are coalesced along the midline. Delthyrial cavity shallower than the deep, bilobed diductor scars that extend to midlength or beyond. Diductor scars are strongly striated radially in well preserved specimens. A low, rounded ridge divides the diductor field. Adductor scars not observed.

DISCUSSION: The genus Boucotella is easily distinguished from other rhynchonelloids externally by its bell-shaped to subtriangular outline and anterior profile, and internally by reduced or absent dental plates and long, bilobed diductor scars in the pedicle valve, and its massive cardinal process in the brachial valve.

Camarotoechia gigantea var. *gigas* Swartz (1929, p. 55, Pl. 6, figs. 29–31) was originally distinguished from normal specimens of *B. gigantea* by its larger size and more abundant plications (26). They represent only large individuals of this species, and are not a distinct taxon.

Boucotella tennesseensis (Roemer, 1890 emended Amsden, 1949, p. 59, Pl. 7, figs. 15–25) from the Brownsport Formation of Tennessee bears a similar type of cardinal process in mature specimens, and the pedicle diductor scars are alike. However, it differs from *B. gigantea* in its more prominent permesothyrid foramen with small deltidial plates in the apex of the delthyrium; the foramen is also sealed off internally. The Keyser species is also larger and has more plications than the Brownsport species.

Sulcatina sulcata (Cooper, 1942), from the Waldron Shale and Laurel Limestone of Indiana, is easily distinguished from *B. gigantea*. *S. sulcata*, the type species of *Sulcatina* Schmidt (1965), is more like *B. tennesseensis* in outline, being more bell shaped to round than subtriangular. Internally, the cardinal process of *S. sulcata* appears to be made of a pair of fused plates (interpreted as chilidial plates by Tillman, 1961) and a bilobed cardinal process, rather than a single pair of plates.

Terebratula stricklandi Sowerby (1839, Pl. 13, figs. 19) from the Wenlock Shale probably belongs to the genus *Boucotella*, but its internal structures are unknown. Compared with *B. gigantea*, it is more bell shaped in outline and more evenly biconvex in lateral profile.

HOLOTYPE: USNM 142842. Keyser Limestone, Devil's Backbone, Maryland.

OCCURRENCE: 17:120–147, 18:110–120, 20:104–110.

STRATIGRAPHIC SECTIONS

Fossils were collected from twenty-six localities of the Keyser Limestone from central Pennsylvania to western Virginia. The localities are shown on Figure 1. The following sections are new and were measured by the writer: Locality 11, West Virginia side of the Potomac River near Dawson, Maryland; Locality 13, Route 46, east of Keyser, West Virginia; Locality 14, New Creek, West Virginia; Locality 21, Section along Route 40, east of Cumberland, Maryland; and Locality 26, Hancock Station, West Virginia. Locality 6, Corriganville, Maryland, and Locality 8, Pinto, Maryland, were redescribed. The other sections were measured by earlier workers and are not redescribed here. Localities 1 to 4 were measured by Reeside (1917). Localities 5, 7, 9–10, 12, 22–25 were measured by C. K. Swartz, and others (1913). Localities 15–20 were measured by F. M. Swartz (1929).

Locality 1, Near Selinsgrove, Pennsylvania: A complete exposure of the Keyser Limestone, 202 feet thick, the overlying New Creek, and the "New Scotland" Limestones occur in the south limb of a broad anticline on the west side of the Susquehanna River, along the Northern Central Railroad, 1 mile north of the railroad junction to Selinsgrove, Pennsylvania. The contact with the Tonoloway Limestone is exposed in a small quarry near the axis of the anticline.

Locality 2, Dalmatia, Pennsylvania: The Keyser is completely exposed in a section 140 feet thick along the Northern Central Railroad, one mile south of Dalmatia, Pennsylvania, on the west side of the Susquehanna River. The New Creek and part of the "New Scotland" are exposed above the Keyser, and the contact between the Keyser and the Tonoloway is exposed in a quarry at the north end of the outcrop. The hanging wall at the south end of the quarry is part of the lower Keyser.

Locality 3, Near New Bloomfield, Pennsylvania: Approximately 140 feet of the Keyser Limestone are exposed 1.7 miles northwest of Route 274 at New Bloomfield on the road to Markelsville, Pennsylvania. The upper boundary of the formation is concealed, but chert and coarse crinoidal intrasparite float from the New Creek and "New Scotland" on the hillside above the Keyser outcrops indicate that only a small amount of the upper Keyser is unexposed. The contact between the Keyser and the Tonoloway is exposed but gradational: it is placed at the first well developed nodular layers. The section is opposite an old mill with a pond on the south side. The railroad which once passed through this section no longer exists.

Locality 4, Mapleton, Pennsylvania: A quarry in the Keyser Limestone on the east side of Route 22 on the east side of the Juniata River opposite the town of Mapleton, Pennsylvania, exposes 153 feet of the Keyser and the contact with the Tonoloway. The quarry is just north of the bridge across the river to Mapleton. The upper boundary of the Keyser is concealed, but most of the *M. praenuntia* Zone and all of the *E. jerseyensis* Zone can be examined. The large face at the southeastern end of the quarry is in the Tonoloway. A thick crinoidal intrasparite near the base of the Keyser varies from 15 to 30 feet thick in various parts of the quarry, thinning to the north.

Locality 5, Hyndman, Pennsylvania: Two exposures of the richly fossiliferous *Gypidula prognostica* peak zone in the *E. jerseyensis* Zone of the Keyser occur along Route 96 on the south side of Hyndman, Pennsylvania. One is in a quarry on the hill west of the intersection of Route 96 with Market Street. In this quarry, just over 100 feet of strata from the *G. prognostica* peak zone to near the base of the formation are exposed. The contact with the Tonoloway is concealed.

The second section is on the southeastern side of Route 96, about 1,000 feet south of the town line. Two small quarries are located on the hill above the level of the highway. A narrow dirt road leads across the stream which is parallel to the highway, around an

abandoned quarry building, and past the quarries. The westernmost outcrop is the
G. *prognostica* peak zone, and the easternmost outcrops are in the Tonoloway Limestone.
The contact between the formations is well exposed in the quarry. This portion of the
Keyser is 120 feet thick.

LOCALITY 6, CORRIGANVILLE, MARYLAND: This section is exposed on the ridge southwest
of Corriganville, Maryland. The upper 207 feet of the Keyser and the entire New Creek
and "New Scotland" Limestones are exposed in a railroad cut of the Western Maryland
Railroad. The cut is in a sharp bend in the railroad on the northeastern side of the hill,
but it can not be seen from the highway, Route 36, below. Swartz (1913, p. 151) measured
the upper 139 feet of the section. An additional 68 feet of the Keyser below that
measured by Swartz were measured by the writer. The entire section is as follows:

"NEW SCOTLAND" FORMATION

Unit	Unit thickness (feet)	Interval above base (feet)
4. Shale, dark-gray, fissile.	25	25–50
3. Limestone, coarse-grained intrasparite, medium-bedded. Chert makes up 75 percent of this unit. *Macropleura macropleura* found at the base.	13	12–25
2. Same as unit 3, but chert less than 50 percent of the unit. Beds 6 to 8 inches thick.	11	1–12
1. Limestone, shaly to limy shale, fissile in part. Contains G. *coeymanensis*.	1	0–1

NEW CREEK LIMESTONE

1. Limestone, coarse-grained, crinoidal, intrasparite, bedding massive. Some chert at top; top 1.5 feet in two layers. Weathers darker gray than Keyser below. Very fossiliferous.	9	0–9

KEYSER LIMESTONE

18. Limestone, light-brown, fine-to-medium-grained, shaly, thinly laminated, weathers platy. A few layers are not banded. Stromatoporoids present at 171–173, 174.5–176.5.	40	167–207
17. Limestone, gray, coarse-grained, bedding massive. Lower part exposed on the south side of the tracks. Stromatoporoids abundant 146–149, 155–167. Lower beds nodular.	27	140–167
16. Limestone, gray, massive when fresh but weathers thin-bedded. Nodular chert or stromatoporoids at top.	10	130–140
15. Limestone, gray, intrasparite, massive but weathers nodular near the base. Chert present in the lower layers.	18	112–130
14. Shale, limy, thin-bedded	1.5	110.5–112
13. Limestone, cherty, shaly, massive, weathers nodular.	5	105.5–110.5
12. Shale, limy, thin-bedded.	1	104.5–105.5
11. Limestone, massive, weathers nodular, contains one thin chert layer.	3.5	101–104.5
10. Limestone, shaly, thin-bedded, with several chert layers. Very shaly at bottom.	6	95–101
9. Limestone, massive, cut by calcite veins.	3.5	91.5–95
8. Limestone, shaly, thin-bedded, nodular. Chert present near top.	16.5	75–91.5
7. Limestone, shaly or limy shale, dark-blue-gray, massive. Brachiopoda: *Gypidula prognostica* at 70 feet, *Eccentricosta jerseyensis*, *Schuchertella deckerensis*, *Nucleospira ventricosa*.	16	59–75

Unit	Unit thickness (feet)	Interval above base (feet)
6. Limestone, shaly, nodular.	6	53–59
5. Limestone, dark-blue-gray, bedding massive.	4	49–53
4. Limestone, very shaly, fissile, with chert.	8	41–49
3. Limestone, dark-blue-gray, intrasparite, bedding massive.	8	33–41
2. Limestone, shaly, nodular. Brachiopoda: *Dolerorthis marylandica, Atrypa reticularis, Delthyris hyndmanensis, Gypidula prognostica, Cupularostrum convexorus, C. litchfieldensis, Machaeraria whittingtoni, Eccentricosta nondivergens, Rhynchospirina martinensis, Nucleospira ventricosa, Cyrtina dalmani.*	17	16–33
1. Limestone, gray, shaly, massive. Remainder concealed.	16	0–16

LOCALITY 7, LA VALE, MARYLAND: An incomplete section of the Keyser can be examined along Cash Valley Road at the intersection with Henry Drive, north of Route 40 at La Vale, Maryland. Neither the upper nor lower boundary of the Keyser is exposed, but approximately 155 feet of the middle beds crop out, including the *G. prognostica* peak zone.

LOCALITY 8, PINTO, MARYLAND: This section is exposed on the north side of the Baltimore and Ohio Railroad, at Pinto, Maryland. Unit 4 is at the east end of the railroad overpass over the road leading into West Virginia. The section is overturned to the west, and the Tonoloway Limestone is exposed farther to the east. Only the lower part of the Keyser is exposed along the tracks, but other isolated outcrops can be seen along the road leading north to Route 220. The upper part of the section was not measured.

KEYSER LIMESTONE

Unit	Unit thickness (feet)	Interval above base (feet)
4. Limestone, dark-blue-gray, bedding massive but weathers nodular. Consists mostly of biomicrite. Extends along the roadside toward Route 220. Brachiopoda: *Schuchertella deckerensis?, Protathyris minuta.*	39	17–56
3. Limestone, nodular, micrite, very thin-bedded, beds 0.5 inch thick, with yellow-brown shale partings. *Brachiopoda: Schuchertella deckerensis?, Protathyris minuta, Cupularostrum litchfieldensis.*	6	11–17
2. Limestone, very shaly to silty, medium-bedded (3 to 6 inches) with several lenses or beds of dark-brown chert. Thin, brown, silty laminations weather in relief on the limestone. This unit resembles beds from 10 to 15 feet above base at Keyser, West Virginia. Brachiopoda: *Schuchertella deckerensis?, Protathyris minuta.*	3.5	7.5–11
1. Limestone, very shaly at top, thin-bedded. Grades into unit 2. Brachiopoda: *Schuchertella deckerensis?, Protathyris minuta, Leptostrophia bipartita nearpassi.*	7.5	0–7.5

Concealed: The contact between the Keyser and Tonoloway is not exposed; but the next rocks cropping out to the east are part of the Tonoloway Limestone.

LOCALITY 9, RAWLINGS, MARYLAND: The upper 75 feet of the Keyser Limestone and the New Creek and "New Scotland" Limestones are exposed along the east side of the Baltimore and Ohio Railroad about 0.75 mile southwest of Rawlings, Maryland on the east flank of Fort Hill. At the bottom of the sequence is a 6-foot thick stromatoporoid bed. Below this bed, the section is faulted and partially concealed by talus, but an additional 40 feet of the Keyser is exposed in the next few hundred feet to the south along the hillside. The contact between the Keyser and New Creek in this section is well exposed.

LOCALITY 10, DAWSON, MARYLAND: The upper 50 feet of the Keyser Limestone are exposed on the Baltimore and Ohio Railroad where it cuts the southwest end of Fort Hill, at Dawson, Maryland. The exposure is on the southeast side of the hill, on the north side of the railroad tracks. A dirt road leads from Route 220 to a tunnel under the railroad, a stream also flows through the tunnel, and past the outcrop. Oriskany Sandstone crops out at the nose of the hill. It is underlain by extensively chertified "New Scotland" and New Creek Limestones. The Keyser is exposed in a small abandoned quarry.

LOCALITY 11, WEST VIRGINIA SIDE OF THE POTOMAC RIVER NEAR DAWSON, MARYLAND: The lower 62 feet of the Keyser are exposed in a section in West Virginia along the Potomac River about 1 mile south of Dawson, Maryland. The outcrop is approximately 0.25 mile south (upstream) of the railroad bridge across the river. The lower nodular part of the Keyser Limestone is exposed in a small syncline. In walking south from the bridge (upstream), the Tonoloway Limestone is first seen in the north limb of the syncline. Overlying the Tonoloway is the nodular Keyser Limestone, but only part of the southern limb of the syncline outcrops. The southern part of the section is exposed along the bank of the river in a nearly vertical face, but it is inaccessible.

KEYSER LIMESTONE

Unit	Unit thickness (feet)	Interval above base (feet)
4. Limestone, shaly, coarse-grained, crinoidal, intrasparite, thin-bedded and nodular. Also seen in the south limb. Brachiopoda: *Atrypa reticularis, Cupularostrum convexorus.*	25	37–62
3. Limestone, mostly fine-grained, nodular, thicker bedded than unit 4. Abundant stromatoporoids and *Favosites* sp., bottom 1 foot crammed with *"Cladopora" rectilineata.* Unit also seen in south limb. Brachiopoda: *Delthyris hyndmanensis, Leptostrophia bipartita nearpassi.*	7	30–37
2. Limestone, fine-grained, thin-bedded, nodular. Contains *Favosites* sp.	25	5–30
1. Limestone, medium to fine-grained, thick bedded. Brachiopoda: *Cupularostrum litchfieldensis.* Concealed for several hundred feet downstream.	5	0–5

TONOLOWAY LIMESTONE

Unit

Limestone, dark-gray but weathering light-brown, fine-grained, thin-bedded, laminated. No crinoidal debris present.

LOCALITY 12, KEYSER, WEST VIRGINIA (TYPE SECTION OF THE KEYSER LIMESTONE): The type section is located in the western quarry of two quarries along the south side of the Baltimore and Ohio Railroad, about 0.33 mile east of Keyser, West Virginia. The two quarries are on the road leading north from Route 46 to Forge Hill. The eastern quarry is in the Tonoloway Limestone. The Keyser-Tonoloway contact is several feet stratigraphically above the large face marking the east side of the western quarry. The contact with the New Creek Limestone can be seen at the western side of the quarry high on the hillside. The thickness of the Keyser is 281 feet.

LOCALITY 13, ROUTE 46, EAST OF KEYSER, WEST VIRGINIA: The lower half of the Keyser outcrops along both sides of Route 46 for several hundred feet east of the eastern town line of Keyser, West Virginia. The interval from the *G. prognostica* peak zone to the contact with the Tonoloway Limestone is exposed on the north side of the highway. This section is only 100 yards along strike from Locality 12, but the degree of weathering is so different that the same units are difficult to recognize in both sections. Differences in the weathering have a remarkable affect on the appearance of the nodular beds and on estimates of the amount of argillaceous material present. When fresh, the nodular limestones appear massive, and without bedding planes; but when weathered, the same beds break into a rubble of limestone pebbles. Fresh exposures of the limy shale and shaly limestone resemble "pure" limestone, and the earlier workers underestimated the amount of shale in the formation. Compare the description of the section below with that for Locality 12, given by C. K. Swartz, and others (1913).

KEYSER LIMESTONE

Unit	Unit thickness (feet)	Interval above base (feet)
Concealed.		
5. Shale, very limy to shaly limestone. Limestone beds 1 to 2 inches thick, interbedded with limy shale layers. Dark-brown chert bands less than 2 inches thick occur in the top 10 to 12 feet. *Gypidula prognostica* peak zone from 131 to 134 feet consists of shaly intrasparite. Brachiopoda: *Atrypa reticularis, Howellella modesta, Cupularostrum litchfieldensis, C. convexorus, G. prognostica.*	31	103–134
4. Limestone, very shaly, dark-blue when fresh, weathers light-brown. Top 4 feet in two beds mottled with shale. Lower beds shaly with interbedded coarse-grained, dark-blue limestone containing abundant fossils. Limestone beds 1 to 2 inches thick, weather blocky, not nodular. Brachiopoda: *Atrypa reticularis, Howellella modesta, Cupularostrum litchfieldensis.*	13	90–103
3. Limestone, shaly, gray, mostly coarse-grained fossil fragmental intrasparite, medium-bedded, nonnodular. Bedding 2 to 4 inches thick in lower 2 feet, followed by 3 feet of thick-bedded limestone. From 72.5 to 78 feet, medium-bedded with abundant crinoid columnals; shaly at top. From 81 to 86 feet distinctly shaly, weathering to dark-blue fissile chips with interbedded lighter colored layers of more resistant limestone containing fossils. Top 4 feet massive and coarse-grained. Brachiopoda: *Nucleospira ventricosa?, Atrypa reticularis, Delthyris hyndamanensis, Gypidula prognostica, Cupularostrum litchfieldensis, Howellella modesta, Schuchertella deckerensis.*	25	65–90
2. Limestone, shaly, dark-gray, mostly medium to fine-grained, massive but weathering nodular; fossil fragments abundant. Some intrasparrudite present. Lower 3 feet very thin-bedded (less than 1 inch thick). Corals abundant from 26 to 28 feet, and at 35 feet and 52 feet. Coarse fossil fragmental intrasparite at 57.5 to 59 feet. Brachiopoda: *Cupularostrum litchfieldensis, C. gordoni, Rhynchospirina martinensis, Protathyris minuta, Howellella vanuxemi, Eccentricosta jerseyensis, Delthyris hyndmanensis, Leptostrophia bipartita nearpassi, Atrypa reticularis, Schuchertella deckerensis, Machaeraria whittingtoni.*	50	15–65

Unit	Unit thickness (feet)	Interval above base (feet)
1. Limestone, medium to fine-grained thin-bedded. Lower 9 feet with shaly bands and dark chert layers 1 inch thick. Beds thicker (2 inches), nonnodular from 9 to 15 feet; these layers also silty and contain more chert. Chert band 5 inches thick at 11 feet. Brachiopoda: *Nucleospira ventricosa?*, *Cupularostrum litchfieldensis*, *Protathyris minuta*.	15	0–15

TONOLOWAY LIMESTONE

Limestone, thinly laminated, fissile; unfossiliferous.

LOCALITY 14, NEW CREEK, WEST VIRGINIA: An excellent exposure of the upper portion of the Keyser Limestone, as well as the New Creek and "New Scotland," is found in an abandoned quarry on the north side of Route 50, 100 yards east of the stream called New Creek, just south of the town of New Creek, West Virginia. The section occurs north of the junction of Route 50 with Route 220. The quarry is now used for gravel and equipment storage by the West Virginia State Roads Division.

ORISKANY FORMATION

Unit	Unit thickness (feet)	Interval above base (feet)
Ridgeley Sandstone Member: Sandstone, gray. Exposed in a small road cut east of the metal bridge over New Creek.		
Shriver Chert Member: Shale, black, containing chert; bedding consists of very nodular layers separated by fissile shale. Exposed in the westernmost part of the quarry. Estimated thickness 45 feet.		

"NEW SCOTLAND" FORMATION

2. Shale, thinly laminated fissile, weathers blackish. Very fossiliferous.	16	31–47
1. Limestone, gray, medium-to coarse-grained intrasparite, very cherty, medium-bedded (4 to 6 inches). Chert lenses and "beds" abundant, vary in color from light blue to nearly black. Bedding surfaces rough and irregular but prominent. Fossiliferous. Silicified brachiopods occur near the top. *Macropleura macropleura* occurs 10 feet above the base.	31	0–31

NEW CREEK LIMESTONE: Type section

Limestone, gray, coarse-grained, fossil fragmental intrasparite, bedding massive. Fossil fragments include echinoderm columnals, bryozoans, corals and stromatoporoids. They are especially abundant in the first few feet, and the lower 2 inches appear pebbly. The fossil fragments have been broken and transported. The massiveness of this unit distinguishes it from the medium-bedded "New Scotland" above. The beds between the top of the massive limestone and the first observed *M. macropleura?* contain few fossils and can not be assigned to either formation with confidence on paleontological grounds.	11	0–11

Unit	Unit thickness (feet)	Interval above base (feet)
KEYSER LIMESTONE		
8. Limestone, dark-blue-gray, fine-grained, finely laminated. Weathers light-brown like the Tonoloway. Fossils rare, but fossil fragments are present near the top.	13.5	106–119.5
7. Limestone, dark-gray, medium-to coarse-grained, silty, medium-bedded. Weathers light-gray. Several thin zones of coarse-grained fossil fragmental limestone rich in bryozoans occur in upper half. Black chert nodules scattered throughout. Sandy chert nodules at 22 feet from the top of unit. Ripple marked surface 26.5 feet from the top. Brown silty lines stand out on weathered surface in lower 15 feet.	35	71–106
6. Limestone, shaly, thin-bedded (2 to 3 inches). Grades into overlying unit. Very fossiliferous in lower 10 feet. Lower portion coarse-grained and fossil fragmental. Some black chert nodules are present. Brachiopoda: *Meristella praenuntia, Schuchertella prolifica, Strophonella (Strophonella)* sp., *Cupularostrum gordoni.*	14	57–71
5. Shale, limy, dark-gray, fissile with intercalated solid bands containing fossil fragments. Weathers with light-gray spots and looks nodular.	5.5	51.5–57
4. Limestone, dark-blue, medium-to-coarse-grained, very thick-bedded. Weathers with light-gray spots. A 1-foot bed of stromatoporoids and *Favosites* sp. occurs 8 feet below the top.	20	31.5–51.5

The section is faulted at this stratigraphic horizon at the top of a gully. The bottom portion of the exposure is covered by talus. It is unclear whether the strata on the east side of the gully, at its base, have been faulted or just sharply folded. The cumulative thickness of the units was extended across this interval for convenience, but this does not mean that some strata may not be missing between units 3 and 4.

Unit	Unit thickness (feet)	Interval above base (feet)
3. Limestone, shaly to limy shale, dark-gray, fissile. Brachiopoda: *Dalejina emarginata?*.	8	23.5–31.5
2. Limestone, packed with coral including *Favosites* sp. and *Cyathophyllum?* sp. Brachiopoda: *Rhynchospirina newcreekensis, Nanothyris boucoti, Cupularostrum gordoni, Nucleospira* sp., *Dalejina emarginata?, Howellella vanuxemi, Meristella* sp., and a rhynchonelloid.	6.5	17–23.5
1. Limestone, gray, very coarse-grained, intrasparite, fossil fragmental, thick-bedded. Crinoid columnals abundant. Bottom of this unit is in the nose of a fold. Concealed.	17	0–17

LOCALITY 15, PETERSBURG, WEST VIRGINIA: Both the upper and lower boundaries of the Keyser are well exposed in a section 270 feet thick about 2 miles east of Petersburg, West Virginia, on the north side of Route 220 from 300 to 1000 feet west of the bridge over the South Branch of the Potomac River. The upper few feet of the Tonoloway are exposed on the hillside at the west end of the section. The contact between the New Creek and the Keyser is sharp and easily recognized. The Big Mountain Shale Member of the Keyser is concealed.

LOCALITY 16, BIG MOUNTAIN, WEST VIRGINIA: The section is exposed in a road cut along a road running west from Route 220 to Smoke Hole, just south of the bridge over the South Branch of the Potomac River, north of Upper Track, West Virginia. The outcrop is on the south side of the road, 1.5 miles west of Route 220. The road is dirt here but paved nearer Route 220. The road cut is in Big Mountain, on the eastern limb of the Big Mountain anticline. The Keyser is 243 feet thick, and both the upper and lower contacts are exposed.

LOCALITY 17, LANTZ MOUNTAIN, VIRGINIA: The lower half of the Keyser and the upper Tonoloway are exposed in an overturned section on the west side of Lantz Mountain on Route 250, 4.2 miles northwest (8.8 miles by road) of the intersection of Routes 250 and 220 at Monterey, Virginia. The Keyser-Tonoloway contact crops out in a bend in the old, unpaved road which is cut off by the present highway. The beds crop out on the east side of the old road and the west side of the new highway. The limestones of the Keyser are unusually coarse-grained and shaly in this section, consisting predominantly of argillaceous intrasparites.

LOCALITY 18, MONTEREY, VIRGINIA: A poor exposure of the Keyser Limestone can be seen 0.5 mile east of Monterey, Virginia on Route 250, in a quarry and hillside about 100 yards north of the highway. The beds dip steeply to the northwest. The New Creek and the upper few feet of the Keyser are quarried. The boundary between the two formations is gradational and difficult to locate. The remainder of the Keyser is not continuously or well exposed, but the boundary with the Tonoloway can be seen on the hillside to the east of the quarry.

LOCALITY 19, EAST OF MCDOWELL, VIRGINIA: Both the upper and lower boundaries of the Keyser are exposed along Route 250 on the east side of Bullpasture Mountain, 4 miles east of McDowell, Virginia. The Keyser-Tonoloway contact crops out along the road west of a small quarry on the north side of the highway. The contact with the New Creek occurs in the quarry. The Big Mountain Shale Member of the Keyser crops out near the western edge of the quarry.

LOCALITY 20, NEAR WARM SPRINGS, VIRGINIA: The lower 125 feet of the Keyser are exposed on Route 39, 6 miles west of Warm Springs, Virginia, on the east side of Back Creek Mountain. The abundance of *Gypidula prognostica*, *Atrypa reticularis* and *Boucotella gigantea* in the interval from 100 to 110 feet above the base of the formation is the most prominent feature of this section. The contact between the Keyser and Tonoloway is well marked by the change from thinly laminated to nonlaminated limestone.

LOCALITY 21, SECTION ALONG ROUTE 40, EAST OF CUMBERLAND, MARYLAND: The section is in a small quarry on the north side of the road leading to Mount Pleasant Church from Route 40 about 2.25 miles east of Cumberland, Maryland. The quarry is several hundred feet north of Route 40, and north of the bridge over Elk Lick Run which passes under Route 40 west of the Baltimore Pike Fire House. The section is also exposed along the south side of Route 40. There are several small isolated outcrops of Helderberg and Keyser Limestone to the west of the quarry toward another quarry in the Oriskany Formation. Approximately the lower 25 feet of the Keyser are concealed, but the Tonoloway Limestone crops out in the stream bed on the south side of Route 40.

KEYSER LIMESTONE

	Unit thickness (feet)	Interval above base (feet)
Unit		
Concealed.		
11. Limestone, shaly, thin-bedded to massive, nodular. Coarse-grained, crinoidal layers 1 to 5 inches thick at bottom. More massive and thick-bedded upward, with coarse-grained limestone in three 3–foot thick nodular		

Unit	Unit thickness (feet)	Interval above base (feet)
layers in the upper 20 feet. *Gypidula prognostica* occurs 3 feet from the top of the section in a thick, limy shale layer. This layer forms the western face (hanging wall) of the quarry. Much of the unit is concealed by mud. Brachiopoda: *Atrypa reticularis, Howellella modesta, G. prognostica.*	44	96–140
10. Limestone, like unit 9 but not as thin-bedded or shaly. Abundant silicified crinoidal debris. Brachiopoda: *Nucleospira ventricosa.*	5	91–96
9. Limestone, very shaly, thin-bedded, nodular. Brachiopoda: *Nucleospira ventricosa.*	4	87–91
8. Limestone, dark-gray, coarse-grained, crinoidal intrasparite, thick-bedded to massive, filled with silicified crinoidal debris. Shaly in top 4 feet where limestone is finer-grained and weathers light-brown. *"Cladopora" rectilineata* occurs 2.5 feet above base. Above this is a 2-foot thick zone with *Favosites* sp. and stromatoporoids. Beds for the next two feet are more shaly and nodular. This unit is also exposed on the south side of Route 40. Brachiopoda: *Nucleospira ventricosa, Atrypa reticularis, Cupularostrum convexorus, Leptostrophia bipartita nearpassi.*	28	59–87
7. Limestone, shaly, fine-grained, thin-bedded, nodular. Brachiopoda: *Leptostrophia bipartita nearpassi.*	2.5	56.5–59
6. Limestone, massive to very thick-bedded. Unfossiliferous.	8	48.5–56.5
5. Limestone, nodular, with light-brown shaly partings.	3.5	45–48.5
4. Limestone, coarse-grained, massive but weathers nodular. In some parts nodules weather lighter gray than remainder of the rock. At 43 feet, a zone 6 inches thick contains *Favosites* sp., stromatoporoids and rugose corals. Brachiopoda: *Schuchertella deckerensis, Rhynchospirina martinensis, Protathyris minuta.*	19	26–45
3. Limestone, thin-bedded, nodular, with light-brown weathering shale partings. Brachiopoda: *Schuchertella deckerensis, Rhynchospirina martinensis, Protathyris minuta.*	5	21–26
2. Limestone, gray, coarse-grained, massive unit. Contains *Favosites* sp.	4	17–21
1. Limestone, fine-grained, thin-bedded, nodular. Light-brown shale partings separate nodular layers. Brachiopoda: *Rhynchospirina martinensis.* Concealed.	17	0–17

LOCALITY 22, SECTION ALONG ROUTE 40 ON EAST SIDE OF MARTIN MOUNTAIN, MARYLAND: This section is located about 0.25 mile east of the top of Martin Mountain on Route 40. The exposure is on the north side of the road; the upper part of the section is on the new Route 40, the lower part is exposed on a remnant of the old Route 40 where it is crossed by the new highway.

The road cut is fresh and the contacts between the Keyser, New Creek, "New Scotland," and Oriskany were not recognized. Therefore, only the lower 200 feet or so can be considered Keyser Limestone with confidence. Limestone extends at least 80 feet higher, but becomes very shaly toward the top. Chert layers are also present near the top.

These beds appear to grade into the Oriskany Formation. Because the exposure is fresh, most of the units appear to be unfossiliferous.

LOCALITY 23, FLINTSTONE, MARYLAND: The lower 200 feet of the Keyser are exposed in two incomplete sections on the east side of Flintstone, Maryland. One is exposed along the south side of Flintstone Creek beginning east of the sharp bend in the stream and extending to 400 feet east of the last house along the old highway of Route 40. This old highway is covered by the new Route 40 at this point. The second section is along the north side of the new highway and along portions of the old road not covered by the new.

LOCALITY 24, SECTION ON TONOLOWAY RIDGE ALONG THE WESTERN MARYLAND RAILROAD: This fine section is located along the Western Maryland Railroad, east of Woodmont, Maryland, in a cut through the south end of Tonoloway Ridge, opposite Great Cacapon, West Virginia. The section begins just west of the lock house on the Chesapeake and Ohio Canal. The section is east of the tool house beside the railroad (=Tonoloway Station?). The Tonoloway Limestone is exposed 10 feet below the lowest Keyser outcrop. The top of the Keyser is not exposed.

LOCALITY 25, HANCOCK, MARYLAND: At Hancock, Maryland, the lower half of the Keyser is exposed in two sections. The lower 55 feet are exposed in a road cut along Route 522 just north of the overpass bridge over Hancock. The overlying 93 feet are exposed along Route 40 and along the ramp leading south from Route 40 to Route 522, 100 feet west of the overpass bridge of Route 522. The uppermost beds represent transitional beds between the two Keyser zones. The Keyser-Tonoloway boundary is exposed along Route 522.

LOCALITY 26, HANCOCK STATION, WEST VIRGINIA: This exposure is on the south side of the Baltimore and Ohio Railroad tracks at Hancock Station, West Virginia, across the river from the town of Hancock, Maryland. The railroad tracks run under the overpass bridge for Route 522, and the section is exposed about 0.33 mile west of the bridge. The section begins about 100 feet east of a telephone pole marked with number 123/30. Neither the top nor the bottom of the Keyser Limestone is exposed here, but these units contain layers with abundant silicified brachiopods belonging to the upper zone of the Keyser. There are several small scattered exposures of crinoidal intrasparite of the lower part of the formation farther west along the tracks.

KEYSER LIMESTONE

Unit	Unit thickness (feet)	Interval above base (feet)
Concealed by debris from Oriskany Formation.		
2. Limestone, very shaly, dull blue-gray, fine-to-medium grained, and limy shale. Like unit 1, but contains more shale, especially near the base. Bedding more massive near the top.	25	41–66
1. Limestone, very shaly, nearly black, fine-to medium-grained, thin-to medium-bedded, and limy shale. The limestone occurs in nodular, lenticular layers 1 to 3 inches thick which weather light-gray. Between the limestone layers are dark-gray limy shale bands which weather dark-gray. From 24 to 41 feet the bedding is more prominent and coarse intrasparite layers 0.5 to 3 inches thick are present which contain silicified brachiopods. Beds with silicified fossils occur at 14 to 15, 28.5, and 31 to 33 feet from the bottom. Unit grades into unit 2. Brachiopoda: *Nanothyris mutabilis, Meristella praenuntia, Cupularostrum gordoni, Rhynchotreta hancockensis.*	41	0–41
Concealed.		

REFERENCES CITED

Alexander, F. E. S., 1949, Revision of the brachiopod species *Anomia reticularis* Linnaeus, genolectotype of *Atrypa* Dalman: Geol. Soc. London Quart. Jour., v. 104, p. 207–220, 2 pls. and figs.

Amsden, T., 1949, Stratigraphy and paleontology of the Brownsport Formation (Silurian) of western Tennessee: Peabody Mus. Nat. Hist. (Yale Univ.) Bull. 5, 138 p., illus.

—— 1951, Brachiopods of the Henryhouse Formation (Silurian) of Oklahoma: Jour. Paleontology, v. 25, p. 69–96

—— 1958, Haragan articulate brachiopods, pt. II [and] Supplement to the Henryhouse brachiopods, pt. III *of* Stratigraphy and paleontology of the Hunton Group in the Arbuckle Mountain region: Oklahoma Geol. Survey Bull. 78, p. 9–158

Amsden, T., and Ventress, W. P. S., 1963, Early Devonian brachiopods of Oklahoma: Oklahoma Geol. Survey Bull. 94, 238 p.

Bancroft, B., 1928, On the notational representation of the rib system in Orthacea: Manchester Lit. Philos. Society, Mem. Proc. v. 72, p. 53–90

Barrande, J., 1847, Über die Brachiopoden der silurischen Schichten von Böhmen: Hard. Natururis. Abh., v. I, p. 1–104

—— 1879, Système Silurian du centre de la Bohême: Prague-Paris, v. 5, 226 p., 1881, v. 6, 342 p.

Barrett, S. T., 1878, The coralline or Niagara Limestone of the Appalachian system as represented at Nearpass Cliff, Montague, New Jersey: Am. Jour. Sci., 3rd ser., v. 15, p. 370–372

Bayle, E., 1878, Explication de la carte géologique de France, v. 4, pt. 1: Paris, 158 pls.

Berdan, J. M., 1949, Brachiopods and ostracods of the Manlius and Cobleskill Limestones of New York: Yale University, Ph.D. dissert.

—— 1963, *Eccentricosta*, a new upper Silurian brachiopod genus: Jour. Paleontology, v. 37, no. 1, p. 254–256, 1 fig.

—— 1964, The Helderberg Group and the position of the Silurian-Devonian boundary in North America: U. S. Geol. Survey Bull. 1180-B, 19 p.

Boucot, A., 1957a, Revision of some Silurian and early Devonian spiriferid genera and erection of Kozlowskiellinae, new subfamily: Senckenbergiana Lethaea, v. 38, p. 311–334

—— 1957b, Position of North Atlantic Silurian-Devonian boundary [abstract]: Geol. Soc. America Bull., v. 68, p. 1702

—— 1959, A new family and genus of Silurian Orthotetacid brachiopods: Jour. Paleontology, v. 33, p. 25–28

—— 1960, Lower Gedinnian brachiopods of Belgium: Univ. Louvain Inst. Géol. Mém., v. 21, p. 279–344, Pls. 9–18

Boucot, A., and Amsden, T., 1958, New genera of brachiopods, pt. IV *in* Stratigraphy and Paleontology of the Hunton Group in the Arbuckle Mountain Region: Oklahoma Geol. Survey Bull. 78, p. 159–190

Bowen, Z. P., 1966, Boucotella, a new Silurian rhynchonelloid brachiopod genus: Jour. Paleontology, v. 40, no. 1, p. 186–189

Branson, E. B., 1922, The Devonian of Missouri: Missouri Bur. Geol. Mines, 2nd ser., v. 17, p. 1–165, illus.

Bronn, H. G., 1862, Die Klassen und Ordnungen der Weichthiere (Malacozoa), v. 3, pt. 1: Leipzig and Heidelberg, 518 p., 44 pls.

Butts, C., 1941, Geology of the Appalachian Valley in Virginia: Virginia Geol. Survey Bull. 52, 568 pp.

Caster, K., 1939, A Devonian fauna from Colombia: Paleontology Bull., v. 24, 218 p.

Cave, R., and Dean, W., 1959, Four British Ordovician species of dalmanelloid brachiopod: Paleontology, v. 1, pt. 4, p. 292–297

Clark, T. H., 1942, Helderberg faunas from the eastern townships of Quebec: Royal Soc. Canada Trans., 3rd ser., Sec. 4, v. 36, p. 11–36, 1 pl.

Cloud, P. E., Jr., 1942, Terebratuloid Brachiopoda of the Silurian and Devonian: Geol. Soc. America Spec. Paper 38, 182 p.

Conrad T. A., 1838, Report on the paleontological department of the survey [of New York]: New York Geol. Survey Ann. Rep. 2, p. 107–119

Cooper, G. A., 1942, New genera of North American brachiopods: Washington Acad. Sci. Jour., v. 32, no. 8, p. 228–235

—— 1944, Brachiopoda, *in* Shimer, H. W., and Shrock, R. R., Index Fossils of North America: New York, Wiley and Sons, p. 277–365

—— 1955, New genera of middle Paleozoic brachiopods: Jour. Paleontology, v. 29, no. 1, p. 45–63

—— 1956, Chazyan and related brachiopods: Smithsonian Misc. Coll., v. 127, pt. 1, p. 1023

Cooper, G. A., and Muir-Wood, H. M., 1951, Brachiopod homonyms: Washington Acad. Sci. Jour., v. 41, no. 6, p. 195–196

Dalman, J. W., 1828, Uppställning och Beskrifning af de i Sverige Funne Terebratuliter: Kongl. Svenska Vetenskapsakad. Handl. 1827, p. 85–155, pls. 1–6

Davidson, Thomas, 1851–1852, British fossil Brachiopoda: The Oolitic and Liasic Brachiopoda: Palaeontogr. Soc., v. 1, pt. 3, 64 p., 13 pl.

—— 1867, A monograph of the British fossil Brachiopoda: Palaentogr. Soc., v. 3, pt. 7, p. 1–397, Pls. 1–50

—— 1881, A monograph of the British fossil Brachiopoda: Palaeontogr. Soc., v. 4, pt. 4, p. 317–368, Pls. 38–42

—— 1882, Supplement to the British Silurian Brachiopoda; A monograph of the British Fossil Brachiopoda: Palaeontogr. Soc., v. 5, p. 63–242

Dunbar, C. O., 1917, *Rensselaerina*, a new genus of lower Devonian brachiopods: Am. Jour. Sci., v. 193, p. 466–470

—— 1919, Stratigraphy and correlation of the Devonian of western Tennessee: Tennessee Geol. Survey Bull. 21, p. 1–127

—— 1920, New species of fossils from western Tennessee: Connecticut Acad. Arts Sci. Trans., v. 23, p. 109–158

Dunbar, C. O., and Condra, G. E., 1932, Brachiopoda of the Pennsylvania System in Nebraska: Nebraska Geol. Survey Bull. 5, 2nd ser., p. 1–377, 44 pls.

Fischer de Waldheim, G., 1830, Oryctographie du gouvernement de Moscou, 1st ed. A. Semen (Moskva), 26 p., 60 pls.

Foerste, A. F., 1903, Silurian and Devonian limestones of western Tennessee: Jour. Geol., v. 11, p. 710

—— 1909, Fossils from the Silurian formations of Tennessee, Indiana and Illinois: Denison Univ. Sci. Lab. Bull., v. 14, p. 61–107

Fuchs, A., 1923, Über die Beziehungen des sauerländischen Faciesgebietes zur belgischen Nord-und Südfacies und ihre Bedentung für das Alter der Verseschichten: Preuss. Geol. Landesanst. Jahrb., v. 42, p. 839–859, 2 figs., 1 pl.

——1929, Beitrag zur kenntnis der unteren Gedinne fauna: Preuss. Geol. Landesanst. Jahrb., v. 50, p. 194–201, Pls. 12–14

Gill, Theodore, 1871, Arrangement of the families of molluscs prepared for the Smithsonian Institution: Smithsonian Misc. Coll., no. 227, 49 p.

Girty, G. H., 1904, New molluscan genera from the Carboniferous: U.S. Natl. Mus. Proc., v. 27, p. 721–736

Grabau, A. W., 1900, Siluro-Devonic contact in Erie County, New York: Geol. Soc. America Bull., v. 11, p. 347–376

—— 1903, Stratigraphy of Becraft Mountain, Columbia County, New York: New York Mus. Bull. 69, p. 1030–1079

Grabau, A. W., and Sherzer, W. H., 1910, The Monroe Formation of southern Michigan and adjoining regions: Michigan Geol. Survey, Geol. ser. 1, pub. 2, 248 p.

Hall, J., 1843, Geology of New York, pt. 4, comprising the survey of the fourth geological district: Natural History of New York, Albany, 683 p.

—— 1852, Containing descriptions of the organic remains of the lower middle division of the New York system (equivalent in part to the Middle Silurian rocks of Europe): Natural History of New York, Paleontology of New York, v. 2, 362 p., 85 pls.

—— 1857, Description of Palaeozoic fossils: New York State Cabinet of Natural History, 10th Ann. Rept., p. 41–186

—— 1858, Contributions to the Palaeontology of New York: New York State Cabinet of Natural History, 12th Ann. Rept., p. 7–62

—— 1859, 1861, Containing descriptions and figures of the organic remains of the Lower Helderberg Group and the Oriskany Sandstone: Natural History of New York, Paleontology of New York, v. 3, pt. 1 (1859), p. 1–532; pt. 2 (1861), 120 pls.

—— 1860, Descriptions of new species of fossils from the Silurian rocks of Nova Scotia: Canadian Naturalist Geologist, v. 5, p. 144–159, figs.

—— 1863, Observations upon some of the Brachiopoda, with reference to the genera *Cryptonella, Centronella, Meristella* and allied forms: Albany Inst. Trans., v. 4, p. 210

—— 1867, Containing descriptions and figures of the fossil Brachiopoda of the Upper Helderberg, Hamilton, Portage, and Chemung Groups: Natural History of New York, Paleontology, v. 4, pt. 1, 427 p.

—— 1879, The fauna of the Niagara Group: New York Mus. Nat. Hist. 28th Ann. Rept., p. 98–203.

Hall, J., and Clarke, J. M., 1892–1895, An introduction to the study of the genera of Palaeozoic Brachiopoda: New York Geol. Survey, v. 8, pt. 1 (1892), p. 1–367, Pls. 1–20; Pt. 2 (1892), p. 1–317; (1895), p. 319–394, Pls. 21–84

Hartnagle, C. A., 1903, Preliminary observations on the Cobleskill ("Coralline") Limestone of New York: New York Mus. Bull. 69, p. 1109–1175

Havlíček, V., 1959, Rhynchonellacea im böhmischen älteren Paläozoikum (Brachiopoda): Věstnik Ústředního ústavu geologického, v. 34

—— 1961, Rhynchonelloidea des böhmischen älteren Paläozoikums (Brachiopoda): Rozpravy Ústředního ústavu geologického, v. 27, 211 p., 27 pls.

Hoar, F. G., and Bowen, Z. P., 1967, Brachiopoda and stratigraphy of the Rondout Formation in the Rosendale Quadrangle, Southeastern, New York: Jour. Paleontology, v. 41, no. 1, 1967 (in press)

Howell, B. F., 1947, Spiriferid brachiopods new to the Silurian Cobleskill Formation of New York: Wagner Free Inst. Bull. Sci., v. 22, 10 p.

Kayser, E., 1871, Die Brachiopoden des Mittel-und ober-Devon der Eifel: Zeitschr. Deutschen geol. Gesell, v. 23, p. 502

King, William, 1846, Remarks on certain genera belonging to the class Palliobranchiata: Annals Mag. Nat. History, v. 18, p. 26–42

—— 1850, A monograph of the Permian fossils of England: Palaeontogr. Soc. Mon. 3, 258 p., 29 pls.

Kozlowski, R., 1929, Les Brachiopodes Gothlandiens de la Podolie Polonaise: Palaeontologia Polonica, v. 1, 254 p.

—— 1946, *Howellella,* a new name for *Crispella* Kozlowski, 1929: Jour. Paleontology, v. 20, p. 295.

Maynard, T. P., 1913, Systematic Paleontology, Lower Devonian, Brachiopoda *in* Lower Devonian Volume (with C. Schuchert): Maryland Geol. Survey, p. 290–449

M'Coy, Frederick, 1844, A synopsis of the characters of the Carboniferous limestone fossils of Ireland: Dublin, 207 p., 29 pls., 34 figs.

McLearn, F. H., 1924, Palaeontology of the Silurian Rocks of Arisaig, Nova Scotia: Canada Geol. Survey Mem. 137, 180 p., 30 pls.

Muir-Wood, H. M., 1925, Notes on the Silurian Brachiopod genera *Delthyris, Uncinulina,* and *Meristina:* Annals and Mag. Nat. Hist., 9th ser., v. 15, p. 83–95

—— 1962, On the morphology and classification of the brachiopod suborder Chonetoidea: London, British Mus. [Nat. Hist.], 132 p., 16 pls.

Nikiforova, O. I., 1937, Brachiopoda of the Cambrian and Silurian Systems of the U.S.S.R.; Upper Silurian Brachiopoda of the Central Asiatic part of U.S.S.R.: U.S.S.R. Central Geol. Prospecting Inst., Paleontology of U.S.S.R. Mon., v. 35, pt. 1, p. 1–94

Oehlert, D. P., 1887, Brachiopodes, pt. 11 *of* Fischer, P. H., Manuel de conchyliologie et de paléontologie conchyliologique, ou Histoire naturelle des mollusques vivants et fossiles: F. Savy, Paris, p. 1189–1334

Öpik, A. A., 1934, Über Klitamboniten: Tartu Univ. (Dorpat), Acta and Commentationes, ser. A., v. 26, no. 3, p. 1–239, 48 pls., 55 figs.

Prouty, W. F., 1923, Systematic paleontology of Silurian deposits, Brachiopoda *in* Silurian Volume (with C. K. Swartz): Maryland Geol. Survey, p. 412–466.

Reeside, J. B., 1917, The Helderberg Limestone of Central Pennsylvania: U.S. Geol. Survey Prof. Paper 108, p. 185–225

Rickard, L. V., 1962, Late Cayugan (Upper Silurian) and Helderbergian (Lower Devonian) stratigraphy in New York: New York Mus. Sci. Service Bull. 386, 157 p.

Roemer, F., 1860, Die Silurische Fauna des Westlichen Tennessee: Breslau, p. 1–97

St. Joseph, J. K. S., 1937, On *Rhynchotreta cuneata* (Dalman) 1828, with a diagnosis of the genus *Rhynchotreta* Hall, 1879: Geol. Mag., v. 74, no. 4, p. 161–176, 6 figs.

Sartenaer, P., 1961a, Etude nouvelle, en deux parties, du genre *Camarotoechia* Hall et Clarke, 1893. Pt. 1, *Atrypa congregata* Conrad, espèce-type (1); Inst. royal. sci. nat. Belgique Bull., v. 37, no. 22, 11 p.

—— 1961b, Etude nouvelle, en deux parties, du genre *Camarotoechia* Hall et Clarke, 1893, Deuxième partie: *Cupularostrum recticostatum* n. gen., n. sp.: Inst. royal sci. nat. Belgique Bull., v. 37, no. 25, 15 p.

Schmidt, H., 1965, Neue Befunde an paläozoischen Rhynchonellacea (Brachiopoda): Senckenbergiana Lethaea, v. 46, no. 1, p. 1–25

Schnur, J., 1853, Zusammenstellung und Beschreibung sämtlicher im Übergangsgebirge der Eifel vorkommenden Brachiopoden: Paleontographica, v. 3, p. 169–248

Schuchert, C., 1897, A synopsis of American fossil Brachiopoda, including bibliography and synonymy: U.S. Geol. Survey Bull. 87, 464 p.

—— 1903, On the Manlius Formation of New York: Am. Geologist, v. 31, no. 3, p. 160–178

—— 1913, Systematic paleontology, Lower Devonian, Brachiopoda, *in* Lower Devonian Volume (with T. P. Maynard): Maryland Geol. Survey, p. 290–449

Schuchert, C., and Cooper, G. A., 1931, Synopsis of the brachiopod genera of the suborders Orthoidea and Pentameroidea, with notes on the Telotremata: Am. Jour. Sci., v. 22, p. 241–251

—— 1932, Brachiopod genera of the suborders Orthoidea and Pentameroidea: Peabody Museum Nat. Hist. (Yale Univ.) Mem., v. 4, pt. 1, 270 p.

Schuchert, C., and LeVene, C. M., 1929, Brachiopoda: Fossilium Catalogus, 1, Animalia, part 42, (Pompeckj, J. F., ed.): Junk, Berlin, 140 p.

Schuchert, C., and Maynard, T. P., 1913, Systematic Paleontology, Lower Devonian, Brachiopoda, *in* Lower Devonian Volume: Maryland Geol. Survey, p. 290–449

Schuchert, C., Swartz, C. K., Maynard, T. P., and Rowe, R. B., 1913, The Lower Devonian deposits of Maryland *in* Lower Devonian Volume: Maryland Geol. Survey, p. 67–95

Sowerby, J., 1816, The mineral conchology of Great Britain, v. 2: London, p. 38, Pl. 118, fig. 3

—— 1839, *in* Murchison, R. I., The Silurian System: London, 768 pp., 36 pls.

Stewart, G. A., 1922, The fauna of the Little Saline Limestone in Ste. Genevieve County: Missouri Bur. Geol. Mines, 2nd ser., v. 17, p. 213–268

Stehli, F. G., 1954, Lower Leonardian Brachiopoda of the Sierra Diablo: Am. Mus. Nat. Hist. Bull., v. 105, art. 3, p. 257–358, illus.

Swartz, C. K., 1913a, Correlation of the Lower Devonian *in* Lower Devonian Volume: Maryland Geol. Survey, p. 96–132.

Swartz, C. K., 1913b, Systematic Paleontology, Lower Devonian, Brachiopoda, *in* Lower Devonian Volume (with C. Schuchert and T. P. Maynard): Maryland Geol. Survey, p. 290–449

—— 1923, Systematic Paleontology of Silurian deposits, Brachiopoda, *in* Silurian Volume (with W. F. Prouty): Maryland Geol. Survey, p. 412–466

—— 1923, Stratigraphic and paleontological relations of the Silurian strata of Maryland *in* Silurian Volume: Maryland Geol. Survey, p. 25–50

Swartz, C. K., Maynard, T. P., Schuchert, C., and Rowe, R. B., 1913, Local Sections *in* Lower Devonian Volume: Maryland Geol. Survey, p. 133–190

Swartz, F. M., 1929, The Helderberg group of parts of West Virginia and Virginia: U.S. Geol. Survey Prof. Paper 158-C, p. 27–74

—— 1939, The Keyser Limestone and Helderberg Group *in* The Devonian of Pennsylvania: Pennsylvania Geol. Survey, 4th ser., Bull. G 19, p. 29–91

—— 1955, Pennsylvania Geologists Guidebook 21st Ann. Field Conf.: Pennsylvania State University, p. S1–8

Swartz, F. M., and Whitmore, F. C., Jr., 1956, Ostracoda of the Silurian Decker and Manlius Limestones in New Jersey and eastern New York: Jour. Paleontology, v. 30, p. 1029–1091

Talent, J. A., 1956, Devonian brachiopods and pelecypods of the Buchan Caves Limestone, Victoria: Royal Soc. Victoria [Australia], Proc. new ser., v. 68, p. 1–54

Tansey, V. O., 1922, The fauna and correlations of the Bailey Limestone in the Little Saline Creek area of Ste. Genevieve County, Missouri: Missouri Geol. and Mines, 2nd ser., v. 17, p. 166–212

Thomas, I., 1910, British Carboniferous Orthotetinae: Geol. Survey Great Britain Mem., Palaeontology, v. 1, pt. 2, p. 83–134

Tillman, C. G., 1961, Stratigraphy and Brachiopod fauna of the Osgood Formation, Laurel Limestone and Waldron Shale of southeastern Indiana: Harvard University, Ph.D. Dissert.

Ulrich, E. O., 1911, Revision of the Paleozoic systems: Geol. Soc. America Bull., v. 22, p. 281–680

Vanuxem, L., 1842, Geology of New York, pt. 3, comprising the survey of the third geological district; Natural History of New York, Albany, 306 p., 80 figs.

Waagen, W., 1882–1885, Salt-Range Fossils, I. Productus Limestone fossils: IV (pt. 1) Brachiopods, 2 vols.: Geol. Survey, India, Mem. Palaeontologia India, ser. 13

Waite, R. H., 1956, Upper Silurian Brachiopoda from the Great Basin: Jour. Paleontology, v. 30, p. 15–18

Weller, S., 1900, A preliminary report on the stratigraphic paleontology of Wallpack Ridge, in Sussex County, New Jersey: N. J. Geol. Survey, Ann. Rep. State Geologist for 1899, p. 1–46

—— 1903, The Paleozoic faunas: New Jersey Geol. Survey, Rep. on Paleontology, v. 3, p. 1–462, 53 pls.

—— 1914, Mississippian Brachiopoda of the Mississippi Valley Basin: Illinois Geol. Survey Mon. 1

White, C. A., 1862, Description of new species of fossils from the Devonian and Carboniferous rocks of the Missisippi Valley: Boston Soc. Nat. Hist. Proc., v. 9, p. 27, Figs. 1–2

Whitfield, R. P., 1882, Descriptions of new species of fossils from Ohio, with remarks on some of the geological formations in which they occur: New York Acad. Sci. Annals, v. 2, p. 193–244

Wilckens, C. F., 1769, Nachricht von selten Versteinerungen: Berlin, p. 78–79, Pl. 8

Williams, A., 1953, North American and European stropheodontids, their morphology and systematics: Geol. Soc. America Mem. 56, 67 p.

Williams, A., and Wright, A. D., 1963, The classification of the "*Orthis testudinaria* Dalman" group of brachiopods: Jour. Paleontology, v. 37, no. 1, p. 1–32

Williams, H. S., 1917, New Brachiopods of the genus *Spirifer* from the Silurian of Maine: U. S. Nat. Mus. Proc., v. 51, p. 73–80.

Manuscript Received by the Society August 31, 1964

EXPLANATION OF PLATES

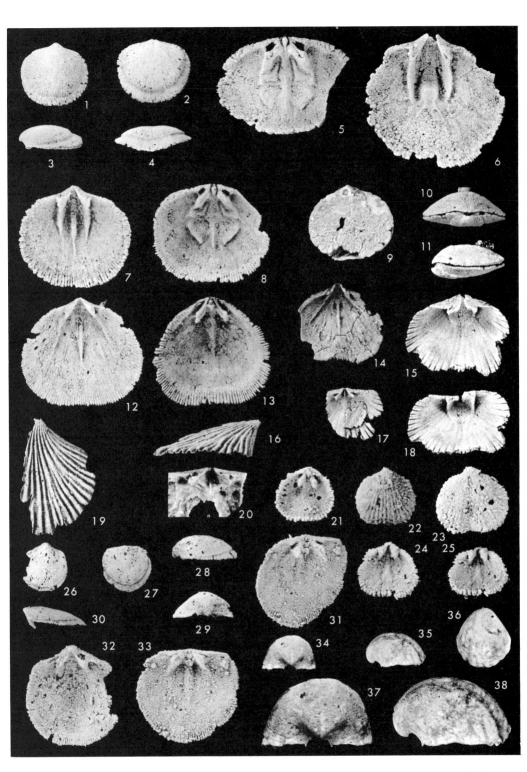

ISORTHIS, DALEJINA, DOLERORTHIS, STRIXELLA, RESSERELLA, AND
GYPIDULA

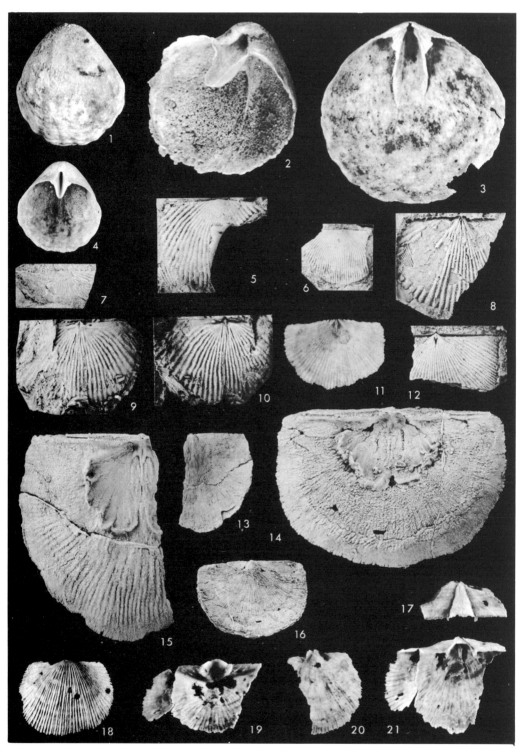

GYPIDULA, ECCENTRICOSTA, STROPHONELLA, AND *SCHUCHERTELLA*

PLATE 2. GYPIDULA, ECCENTRICOSTA, STROPHONELLA, AND SCHUCHERTELLA

Figures   Page

1–4. *Gypidula prognostica* (Maynard, 1913) 24
    1, 4, Exterior and interior views of pedicle valve; MCZ 9443a; 1 (× 1.8), 4
    (× 1.35)
    2, Oblique view of pedicle interior. The median septum supports the spondyl-
    ium only at the posterior. MCZ 9443b (× 2.7)
    3, Brachial interior. The three pairs of plates can be distinguished: the inner
    plates are inclined medially from the valve margins; the brachial process
    plates are concave medially, nearly perpendicular to the shell, their
    anterior ends free; the outer plates, which join the valve bottom, are
    inclined medially. MCZ 9443c (× 2.7)
    Locality 5: Hyndman, Pennsylvania, 116–120 feet

5–6, 9–10. *Eccentricosta jerseyensis* (Weller, 1900) 26
    6, Pedicle exterior; MCZ 9444 (× .9). Locality 4: Mapleton, Pennsylvania, 18–27
    feet
    5, Squeeze of an impression of the pedicle exterior. Note the ribs radiate from
    posterior to the beak and curve anteriorly near the margins. MCZ 9445a
    (× 1.8)
    9–10, Squeeze of impression of brachial interior and the impression from
    which it was made. Note the ridgelike socket walls, bilobed cardinal
    process, and the small diverging septae. MCZ 9445b (× 1.8)
    Locality 25: Hancock, Maryland, 70–99 feet

7–8, 11–12. *Eccentricosta nondivergens* (Swarts and Whitmore, 1956) 27
    7, Pedicle exterior. The ribs are straight, and the spines along the hinge line
    are directed laterally. MCZ 9446a (× 2.7). Locality 25: Hancock, Maryland,
    70–99 feet
    8, Impression of the pedicle interior. Ribs are straight; spines are directed
    posteromedially. Note the impression of the diamond-shaped median
    septum. MCZ 9447 (× 1.8). Locality 16: Big Mountain, West Virginia, Big
    Mountain Shale Member
    11, Pedicle interior; MCZ 9448 (× 1.8). Locality 13: Tonoloway Ridge, Mary-
    land, 10–45 feet
    12, Impression of pedicle interior. Note impression of median septum. MCZ
    9446b (× 1.8). Locality 25: Hancock, Maryland, 70–99 feet

13–16. *Strophonella (Strophonella)* sp. 31
    13, 15, Exterior and interior views of pedicle valve. Note the denticulation.
    MCZ 9449a; 13 (× .9), 15 (× 1.8)
    14, 16, Pedicle interior showing pronounced ridge bordering muscle field and
    papillose inner surface, and exterior of same shell; MCZ 9449b; 14 (× 1.8),
    16 (× .9)
    Locality 24: Tonoloway Ridge, Maryland, 240–266 feet

17–21. *Schuchertella deckerensis* (Weller, 1903) 29
    17, 19, 21, Posterior, inclined interior, and interior views of pedicle valve. Note
    the asymmetry and division of the interarea into inner and outer areas,
    and the strongly convex pseudodeltidium. The teeth are unsupported by
    dental plates in fig. 19. MCZ 9450a (× 2.7)
    18, Brachial exterior; MCZ 9450b (× 1.8)
    20, Brachial exterior; MCZ 9450c (× 1.8)
    Locality 22: Martin Mountain, Maryland, 0–93 feet

PLATE 3. SCHUCHERTELLA AND LEPTOSTROPHIA

    1, 3, Exterior and interior of brachial valve; MCZ 9451a ($\times$ 1.8)

    2, 4, Exterior and interior of pedicle valve; MCZ 9451b ($\times$ 1.8)

    5, Enlargement of the cardinalia showing the quadrilobed posterior face of the cardinal process; MCZ 9451c ($\times$ 2.7)

    6, 7, Normal view of posterior part of pedicle interior showing the strongly arched pseudodeltidium, and inclined view parallel to the interarea of same specimen. The stout teeth are supported only by rodlike thickening along the edge of the delthyrium, but not by dental plates. MCZ 9451d ($\times$ 2.7)

    Locality 12: Keyser, West Virginia, 223–230 feet

    8, Impression of the pedicle interior. Note the denticulate hinge line, large triangular muscle field, tuberculate lateral areas and curved costae. MCZ 9452a ($\times$ 1.8). Locality 25: Hancock, Maryland, 70–99 feet

    9, Pedicle interior; MCZ 9453a ($\times$ 1.8)

    10, Brachial interior. Note denticulate hinge line, socket plates, median ridge, and curved pseudopunctate ribs. MCZ 9453b ($\times$ 1.8)

    Locality 8: Pinto, Maryland, 0–7 feet

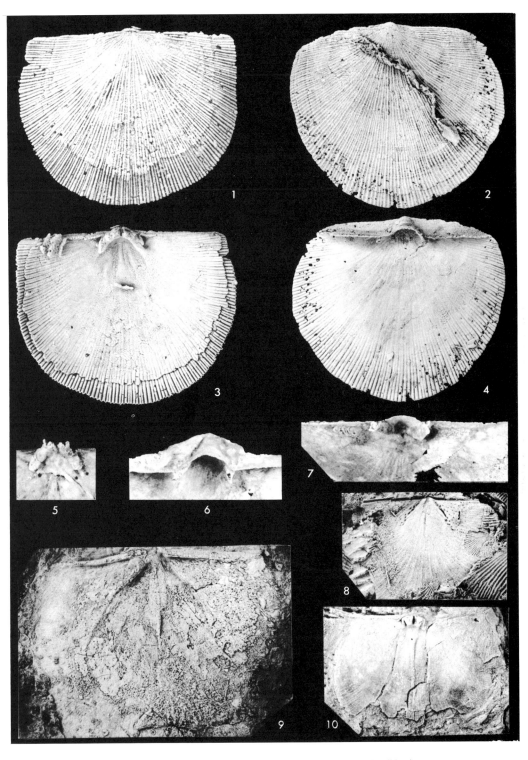

SCHUCHERTELLA AND *LEPTOSTROPHIA*

LEPTOSTROPHIA, LEPTAENA, MERISTA, AND *MERISTELLA*

Plate 4. Leptostrophia, Leptaena, Merista, and Meristella

Figures | Page

1–2. *Leptostrophia bipartita nearpassi* (Barrett, 1878) 30

1, Brachial interior. Bordering the bilobed cardinal process are the small, knoblike socket plates. MCZ 9453c (× 2.7). Locality 8: Pinto, Maryland, 0–7 feet

2, Impression of the pedicle interior. The hinge line is completely denticulate. Note the large pores (corresponding to tuberculae on the shell) bordering the smooth muscle field. MCZ 9452b (× 1.8). Locality 25: Hancock, Maryland, 70–99 feet

3–5. *Leptaena* sp. cf. *L. "rhomboidalis"* (Wilckens, 1769) 32

3, Brachial interior; MCZ 9454a (× 1.8)

5, Brachial interior; MCZ 9454b (× 1.8)

Locality 14: Hancock, Maryland, 70–99 feet

4, Pedicle exterior; MCZ 9455 (× 1.8). Locality 3: New Bloomfield, Pennsylvania

6–9. *Merista* sp. indet. 33

6–9, All pedicle interiors (× 1.8)

6, Ridges from the dental plates are parallel to the "shoe-lifter" process. MCZ 9456. Locality 19: McDowell, Virginia, 57–67 feet

7, Elongate specimen with the ridges running onto the "shoe-lifter" process only anteriorly; MCZ 9457. Locality 16: Big Mountain, West Virginia, 114–135 feet

8, Ridges run onto the "shoe-lifter" nearer the posterior. MCZ 9458. Locality 20: Warm Springs, Virginia. 100–102 feet

9, Ridges run onto the process immediately anterior to the delthyrial cavity. MCZ 9459. Locality 23: Flintstone, Maryland

10–22. *Meristella praenuntia* Schuchert, 1913 34

10–12, 17, Brachial, anterior, posterior, and lateral views of a small specimen; MCZ 9460a (× 1.8)

15, Pedicle exterior; MCZ 9460c (× 1.8)

16, 18, Lateral and interior views of pedicle valve. Note foramen, teeth and triangular diductor scar. MCZ 9460b (× 1.8)

19, Brachial interior. Stout cruralium developed on a well-developed septum. The cruralium has no cover. MCZ 9460d (× 1.8)

Locality 14: New Creek, West Virginia, 57–71 feet

13–14, Pedicle and lateral view of typical specimen which also shows spires; MCZ 9461 (× 1.8)

20, Brachial interior (× 1.8)

21, Pedicle interior, inclined views. The deep diductor scar expands rapidly anterior of the termination of the short dental plates. (× 1.8)

22, Pedicle interior of a narrow specimen. (× 1.8)

Locality 24: Tonoloway Ridge, Maryland

PROTATHYRIS, RHYNCHOSPIRINA, NUCLEOSPIRA, AND *ATRYPA*

ATRYPA, KOZLOWSKIELLINA, CYRTINA, HOWELLELLA, AND *DELTHYRIS*

PLATE 6. ATRYPA, KOZLOWSKIELLINA, CYRTINA, HOWELLELLA, AND DELTHYRIS

Figures　　　　　　　　　　　　　　　　　　　　　　　　　　　　　　　　　　　Page

1–5. *Atrypa reticularis* (Linné, 1758) 41
    1, 5, Exterior and interior views of pedicle valve. Note the bifurcating ribs.
       MCZ 9476a; 1 (× .9), 5 (× 1.8)
    2, 3, Inclined and normal views of brachial interior. Note the ridge within
       each socket and the absence of a deposit in the notothyrial cavity. MCZ
       9476b (× 1.8)
    4, Pedicle interior; MCZ 9476c (× 1.8)
    Locality 6: Corriganville, Maryland, 16–33 feet
6–8. *Kozlowskiellina* (*Megakozlowskiella*) *praenuntia* (Swartz, 1929) 45
    6, Brachial exterior. Note the frilly lamellae. MCZ 9477 (× 1.8). Locality
       24: Tonoloway Ridge, Maryland, 218–230 feet
    7, 8, Interior and exterior views of brachial valve; MCZ 9478; 7 (× 1.8), 8 (× 2.7).
    Locality 24: Tonoloway Ridge, Maryland, 240–266 feet
9–20. *Cyrtina dalmani* (Hall, 1857) 44
    9–10, Posterior view showing large interarea and narrow delthyrium, and
       pedicle view of a coarsely silicified but complete shell; MCZ 9479a (× 2.7)
    11, Pedicle view; MCZ 9479b (× 4.05)
    12–14, Posterior view and inclined views of the interior of a pedicle valve
       showing the hollow tichorhinum and the incomplete longitudinal septum.
       The left part of the tube is bent so that the tichorhinum appears bent.
       MCZ 9479c (× 2.7)
    15, Brachial interior; MCZ 9479d (× 4.05)
    16, Brachial exterior; MCZ 9479e (× 4.05)
    17, Brachial interior showing cardinalia; crura missing; MCZ 9479f (× 4.05)
    Locality 16: Big Mountain, West Virginia, 185–198 feet
    18–20, Posterior, lateral, and brachial views; MCZ 9480 (× 2.7). Locality 6:
    Corriganville, Maryland, 16–33 feet
21–28. *Howellella modesta* (Hall, 1857) 47
    21–24, Pedicle, lateral, posterior, and anterior views of a typical specimen;
       MCZ 9481a (× 1.8)
    25, Brachial view; MCZ 9481b (× 1.8)
    26, Pedicle view of a less transverse specimen; MCZ 9481c (× 1.8)
    Locality 12: Keyser, West Virginia, 90–133 feet
    27, Pedicle interior showing well-developed dental plates which extend as
       ridges bordering the muscle field. Note the delthyrium is bordered
       laterally by small deltidial plates and apically by a small convex deposit.
       MCZ 9483a (× 1.8)
    28, Brachial interior. The crural plates join with the floor of the valve. MCZ
       9482b (× 1.8)
    Locality 5: Hyndman, Pennsylvania, 116–120 feet
29–33. *Howellella vanuxemi* (Hall, 1859) 48
    29, Pedicle view; MCZ 9483a (× 2.7)
    30, Pedicle view. Lateral ribs are well developed. MCZ 9483b (× 1.8)
    Locality 9: Rawlings, Maryland, 6.5–10 feet
    31, Pedicle interior. Dental plates do not extend forward as low ridges as in
       H. modesta. MCZ 9484 (× 1.8). Locality 24: Tonoloway Ridge, Maryland,
       10–45 feet
    32–33, Normal and oblique views of brachial interior. Note that the crural
       plates join the bottom of the shell only at the posterior. MCZ 9485 (× 2.7).
       Locality 16: Big Mountain, West Virginia, 185–198 feet
34–43. *Delthyris hyndmanenis* n. sp. 50
    34, Oblique view of pedicle interior. Note the high, abruptly ending septum
       which is swollen at the posterior. Prominent dental plates define large
       umbonal cavities. MCZ 9486a (× 1.8)
    35–37, Lateral, pedicle, and interior views of the holotype showing incurved
       beak and large blunt teeth; MCZ 9486b; 35, 37 (× 1.35), 36 (× 1.8)
    38–43, Anterior, inclined interior, exterior, lateral, posterior, and normal in-
       terior views of brachial valve. Note the stout socket walls and the crural
       plates which join the bottom of the shell only at the posterior. MCZ
       9486c; 38–40, 42–43 (× 1.8), 41 (× 1.35)
    Locality 5: Hyndman, Pennsylvania, 116–120 feet

NANOTHYRIS, RHYNCHOTRETA, AND *CUPULAROSTRUM*

CUPULAROSTRUM, BOUCOTELLA, AND MACHAERARIA

PLATE 8. CUPULAROSTRUM, BOUCOTELLA, AND MACHAERARIA

Figures | Page

1–2. *Cupularostrum gordoni* (Maynard, 1913) 57

1–2, Pedicle and lateral views of an internal mold. Note the bifurcations of the lateral pallial trunks, and the large muscle (?) scars. MCZ 9496h (× 1.8)

Locality 14: New Creek, West Virginia, 57–71 feet

3–7. *C. convexorus* (Maynard, 1913) 61

3, Brachial interior showing partially roofed-over septalium; MCZ 9497a (× 1.8)

4, Pedicle valve with thin dental plates; MCZ 9497b (× 1.8)

Locality 5: Hyndman, Pennsylvania, 116–120 feet

5–7, Brachial, lateral, and front views; MCZ 9498 (× 1.8). Locality 12: Keyser, West Virginia, 90–133 feet (?)

8–20. *Boucotella gigantea* (Maynard, 1913) 63

8–12, Pedicle, lateral, brachial, posterior, anterior views. The beak is broken, not perforate. MCZ 9499 (× .9). Locality 20: Warm Springs, Virginia, 104–110 feet

13–17, Normal, oblique anterior, posterior, perpendicular, and lateral views of the cardinal process; MCZ 9500a (× 1.8)

18, View of umbonal area of a broken specimen showing the cardinal process in place; MCZ 9500b (× 1.8)

Locality 17: Lantz Mountain, Virginia, 120–147 feet

19, 20, Normal and inclined view of pedicle interior; MCZ 9501 (× 1.8). Locality 18: Monterey, Virginia

21–29. *Machaeraria whittingtoni* n. sp. 62

21–22, 28, Pedicle, posterior, and lateral views of holotype. Note large foramen and straight beak. MCZ 9502a (× 1.8)

23–24, Anterior and brachial views of a specimen with four plications on the fold; MCZ 9502b (× 1.8)

25, 29, Inclined and normal views of brachial interior. Note the thin, blade-like cardinal process between the divided hinge plates. MCZ 9502c (× 1.8)

26–27, Inclined and normal views of the pedicle interior. Note the well-developed dental plates. MCZ 9502d (× 1.8)

Locality 5: Hyndman, Pennsylvania, 116–120 feet

INDEX